A Dictionary of Science

Guidelines for using the this dictionary:

1. If you can't find a word that has a prefix (e ...) is no antidiuretic .. try diuretic.
2. Don't just use it to look up word that you ... In that way you will come across definitions ...
3. Make a distinction between learning what w ... banana, and understanding the idea referred to by a word ... force, pressure, current.
4. Definitions can't be read in the way you would read a short story. There is just too much information per sentence and so a definition may need to be read through more than once. Read the first time to get a feeling of the meaning, then go back and check the main ideas, then look for the extra bits that have been trapped between commas or brackets). Try this technique on the definition of aurora borealis below:

Aurora borealis (Northern lights)   Shimmering lights (usually in reds and greens) in the form of streamers and curtains which can appear over the north and south poles. They are produced when fast moving charged particles from the sun (see solar wind) collide with particles in the earth's atmosphere and cause them to glow.

Guidelines followed while writing this dictionary:

1. Definitions need to be simple but not so simple that the facts are distorted. One way around this is to make the definition progressively harder. Have a look at anaerobic to see an example of how the definition becomes progressively more detailed and precise (rigorous).
2. The reader should not have to look up lots of other words while they are finding out about the one they want. This is not always possible.
3. To put in words which are just generally interesting e.g. bad breath even though they might not be part of any science syllabus.
4. Space is a problem because the dictionary can't be much longer that about 128 pages without beccomming quite expensive (most printers work with sheets of paper large enough to hold 16 book pages. Books tend to increase in jumps of 16 or 32. It is often almost as expensive to add 4 pages to a book as it is to add 16).

Common English words which have particular relevance to science

Analogy   A comparison   Example which is meant to be helpful but which may introduce incorrect comparisons.   We need to be very careful about using analogies because they can be helpful but are traps for the unwary.

Arbitrary   Decided on a whim. i.e. we may use arbitrary units on a graph. These would be units which act more as simple guidelines rather than giving precise information about the sets of coordinates.

Anthropomorphic   Giving human attributes to non human organisms or to inanimate objects.   We may believe that bloodhounds feel sad because of the set of their faces or claim that the mineral agate is sympathetic to children. Seeing the rest of the animal kingdom from our perspective can cause problems e.g. we may put earthworms in a box close to the radiator because 'they can't possibly like living in the cold damp soil.

Common English words which have particular relevance to science

Dependant variable As we know; tar becomes more runny as the temperature rises. The 'runniness' (viscosity) is dependant on temperature and if we were plotting a graph the temperature (the independent variable) would be on the x axis and runniness would be on the y axis. In the case of $y = 7x$, the value of y is dependant on the value of x so y is the dependant variable.

Emotive words If a number of you are having a discussion in which you are trying to get to the truth, it is not helpful to use words which make the others cross or agitated, i.e. emotive words. Science has eliminated many of the emotive words that it used in the old days (i.e. a few centuries ago). In chemistry now the only remaining emotive words are **base** and **noble** metals. If all you want is an adrenaline high, then a shouting match is one way to get it, but it is not the way to find out the truth.

Fact A fact is something that is known to be true or something that has happened. History shows that we need to be very careful about facts. Mistakes are easily made so that some of the 'facts' like 'The Earth is flat', 'Witches can cause the crops to fail', 'The Earth is at the centre of the solar system', which were once believed to be true but are now known to be suspect.

Hypothesis This is a suggestion as to how something might work. Once you have such a suggestion, you can design experiments which will prove or disprove the hypothesis.

Observation: Bats sometimes get caught up in people's hair.

Hypothesis: The loose hair around the head doesn't reflect the squeaks sent out by bats well enough for them to detect the hair.

A possible Experiment: Use a signal generator to mimic bat sounds and direct these at a number of different similar-sized objects including the heads of people with lots of stray hair. Collect the reflections and compare the strengths. Have a look at bats normal food to find whether any of these animals make themselves 'invisible' by covering themselves with fur (there are some furry moths).

Hyper- A prefix meaning 'above' as in hypertonic i.e. a solution which has a greater osmotic pressure than another is said to be hypertonic. Sea water is hypertonic to our body fluids.

Hypo- A prefix indicating 'below'. e.g. 1. many injections are administered hypodermically, i.e. below the skin. e.g. 2. our body fluids are hypotonic to sea water.

Inter- A prefix meaning 'between'. It is used by British Rail for their Intercity service which travels between certain cities. Scientific examples are: intergalactic space, interface (a boundary between two parts of any system), interpolation (the process of filling in values between two known values).

Intra- A prefix denoting within: Intra-muscular injection is one into muscle, intra-molecular forces are those that exist between molecules.

Jargon This is the specialised language concerned with a particular subject. A lot of the words that we use in everyday language have more than one meaning and so are not really suitable for use in science, where each word should have only one precise meaning. For this reason, jargon is used. It can sometimes be misused though by using is to frighten the audience rather than to clarify the subject. People can 'hide behind' the jargon, i.e. when they are asked a difficult question, they use lots of jargon, hoping that the others will be too nervous to ask for definitions. Never be afraid to ask someone to define their terms, you will be surprised how often they can't do so!

Law A rule that governs the behaviour of matter or events, e.g. Newton's first law of motion.

Common English words which have particular relevance to science

Objective When someone is being objective they are trying to stop their emotions from interfering with any decisions. They allow the facts to decide the issue. They are impartial. Scientists should try very hard to be objective but it is not that easy to achieve. We often only see what we expect to find e.g. we're in the kitchen needing the scissors. We 'know' that they are in the bedroom and so only have a quick look around and then a thorough hunt in the bedroom with no luck. On returning to the kitchen we see them on the table right where we were working; we often see what we expect to see.

Prediction A prophesy, a statement about what may happen. In science, predictions should be based on the observations that have been collected. Predictions allow us to test theories e.g. the kinetic theory suggests that particles speed up as the temperature rises. We can predict that they will bounce harder and so pressure will rise. This can be tested and if pressure does rise as temperature rises, we have some support for our theory.

– philic having a love (affinity) for something e.g. many organic substances are lipophilic i.e. oils stick to their surfaces or they dissolve in oils.

– phobic having a hate for something e.g. oils are hydrophobic. Thy do not mix well with water.

Principle This is a fundamental truth or a rule or law which is assumed to be true or which has been proved to be true. In maths we can prove that it doesn't matter in which order two numbers are added together, the answer will be the same in each case, i.e. a + b = b + a is known as the commutative principle.

Prognosis This is a forecast, usually used by medics to indicate the course that a particular disease will follow. A friend, who knows how hard and how effectively you have worked at science all year, may say when asked about your chances in the forthcoming exams 'The prognosis is good'.

quantitative

It's **42° C**!

It is **very hot** today !

qualitative

Qualitative An assessment of amount or size (or extent) which does not use figures. Its deals just with qualities like tall or short.

Quantitative In this case we are concerned with quantities, i.e. actual numerical values like 2·13 m or 1·25 cm .

Subjective Allowing personal feelings to influence one's judgment or decisions sometimes in an unfair way.

Theory Whereas an hypothesis is used as a basis for further investigation, a theory is an explanation, based on carefully thought out ideas, which now forms an important part of a subject. The theory may be good and yet still not work in practice because in the outside world, there are more variables than may have been taken into account when the theory was devised.

Variable A variable is anything which can change e.g. temperature, pressure, food supply, sunlight, surface area of reactants etc. In science we try to study only a few variables at any one time. If we were working with a gas, we might see how pressure affects volume and when we did this we would keep everything else constant.

Some of the people who do physics tend to be a little arrogant about their nice crisp subject. They fail to grasp how difficult it can be to control all the variables in the applied sciences like sociology. Sociology seems messy to them, it is messy, but that doesn't make it any less valuable.

In physics and chemistry it is fairly simple to control the variables but not in biology. It is even harder in ecology and it becomes a nightmare to try and keep track of the variables in a subject like sociology: If you are studying children with behaviour problems you have to take account of the home environment, the amount of lead in the air from passing cars, their genes, the tele. programmes that they watch . . . the list seems endless !

Absolute units   An absolute unit has an unchanging value at all times and places. See the table of basic SI units and derived SI units at the back of the book.

Three absolute units (SI scale)	
centimetre	for length
gram	for mass
second	for time

Absolute value   Absolute values can be shown on the number line as the distance out from zero.   2 is the absolute value of both +2 and –2

```
     -3  -2  -1   0   1   2   3
      |   |   |   |   |   |   |
          |←—|—→|←—|—→|
```

Absolute zero   The lowest possible temperature.   As a substance cools down, atoms and molecules vibrate more slowly. When they finally stop, that lump of matter has reached the lowest temperature that is possible for it; you can't go any slower than stop! This temperature is 0 on the Kelvin scale   (the degree symbol is not used with the Kelvin scale). $0 K = -273.15°C$

Absorbtance   A measure of the ability of a substance to absorb radiation. An ideal black body has an absorbtance of 100% (see also black body).

Absorption spectrum   The spectrum that appears on the chart recorder, screen (or on film) shows dark bands because that part of the spectrum has been absorbed by the test substance. In general the substance absorbs those wavelengths which it would emit if it was heated until it glowed brightly.

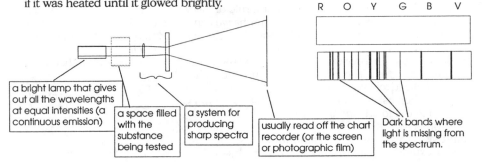

a bright lamp that gives out all the wavelengths at equal intensities (a continuous emission)

a space filled with the substance being tested

a system for producing sharp spectra

usually read off the chart recorder (or the screen or photographic film)

Dark bands where light is missing from the spectrum.

Abyssal   An adjective applied to organisms that inhabit deep water, below 1000 metres.

Acceleration   This happens whenever objects **slow down, speed up** or **change direction.** Two things are involved: there is the change in **velocity** and there is the time for the change to happen. Acceleration is the rate of change of velocity with time. (suitable units: metres per sec. per sec. i.e. ms^{-2})

$$a = \frac{v - u}{t}$$

Accelerator   A device for speeding up charged particles (electrons, protons or ions). The particles are made to speed up in an electric field and are then kept moving in the desired direction by a magnetic field. The particle can be made to move in a straight line (linear acceleration) or follow a circular path.

Accommodation   Most of the bending of light that enters your eyes is done by the **cornea.** The lens does the final focusing and this fine tuning is known as accommodation. What happens is this: when you glance up from this page and look out of the window, the distant view is fuzzy for 0.5 seconds. In that time two things happen: for about 0.16 seconds your eyes diverge (look further apart), then for about 0.36 seconds the lens focuses the image on the retina. Unless you concentrate, you do not even notice that, for a while, the picture is out of focus.

muscles for adjusting the lens thickness

cornea

this is the surface that changes during focussing

retinal surface

Accumulator The most common accumulator today is the car lead acid battery. When electricity is passed through it in one direction, chemical changes take place at the electrodes. These changes are reversed when current is drawn from the battery (see also batteries, cells and electrolysis).

Paramecium caudatum

Acellular **1.** In certain organisms (e.g. many fungi) and tissues (e.g. striated muscle) there are many nuclei, but no cell membranes or other divisions can be seen between them. It looks as though the divisions may once have been there but have now disappeared.
2. The protozoan organisms (Amoebae, Euglena, Paramecium etc.) have only one nucleus but are slightly too complicated to be thought of as simple cells. Some scientists think of them as unicellular but others prefer the term acellular.

0.25 mm

Acetic acid This is the old name for ethanoic acid. Vinegar is 2–4% ethanoic acid. Ethanoic acid: CH_3CO_2H .

Achromatic lens A single lens will act like a prism and so the light passing through it will be split into many tiny spectra. This only becomes a problem when two or more lenses are used together because the effect then becomes noticeable (chromatic aberration). Fortunately it is possible to almost eliminate the effect by using lenses made from different sorts of glass. Such lenses are said to be achromatic.

Acid All acids contain hydrogen. They react with water to form a solution of hydrogen ions ($H^+_{(aq)}$) (aqueous hydrogen ions). An acid dissolves in water to give a pH less than pH 7, and turns litmus red. Acids react in very predictable ways:

Acid	+	Reactive metal	=	Salt	+	Hydrogen
Acid	+	Metal oxide	=	Salt	+	Water
Acid	+	Metal hydroxide	=	Salt	+	Water
Acid	+	Metal carbonate	=	Salt	+	Carbon dioxide + Water

(acids act as proton donors i.e. they give off hydrogen ions)

Acid rain This term is used to describe rain which has a pH of less than 5·6. The rain becomes contaminated with sulphur dioxide (from the burning of coal) or with nitrogen oxides and sulphur dioxide (from motor car exhausts). Sulphuric acid and nitric acid are the main acids found in acid rain. Unpolluted rain contains dissolved carbon dioxide which gives it a pH of 5·6 or above. Acid rain has three main effects: a. It can cause positive ions to leach from the soil into the streams. When Mg^{++} are leached from soil the plants in the region have difficulty making chlorophyll and so turn increasingly yellow and die. b. It increases the corrosion rates on buildings and metal structures. c. Acids in the air are breathed in, dissolve in the fluid that lines the respiratory tract and then damages the cells. Asthma and bronchitis can result.

Acoustics The study of sound.

Acquired characteristics These are physical characteristics acquired during the lifetime of an individual e.g. the stunted form of a plant growing in very poor soil, callouses on the hands of a gardener or the well developed muscles of a weight lifter. **Such characteristics are not passed on to their offspring**.

Acre 4840 square yards e.g. plot that is about 70 yards by 70 yards. The acre is a British unit. The metric unit is the hectare (10 000 m²). 1 hectare = 2·47105 acres.

Acrosome Found at the tip of the sperm, it is responsible for dissolving the outer layer of the egg during fertilisation.

Actin One of the proteins found in muscle. Fibres of actin and myosin can slide over each other when stimulated so that the muscle shortens.

Activated carbon When charcoal is treated with very hot steam, air or CO_2 it becomes very absorptive and can be used to absorb impurities .

Activated sludge In one method of sewage treatment the sewage is vigorously aerated. With plenty of oxygen present, bacteria and protozoa rapidly digest the sewage and use the nutrients to multiply. This rich mixture of bacteria and protozoa is termed activated sludge and some of it is then added to the next batch of sewage. In this way the treatment of sewage is speeded up.

Activation energy We call the energy needed to start the reaction activation energy, because without it no reaction would take place.

Graph showing the energy transfers taking place during the burning of ethane.

Activation energy i.e. the energy needed to break the bonds in the ethane and oxygen

uncatalysed reaction

energy given out when the bonds reform giving carbon dioxide and water

catalysed reaction

energy transfers (arbitrary units)

this amount of energy has been released as a result of burning the ethane

time (as the reaction proceeds) (arbitrary units)

Active site See enzyme.

Active transport Cells can control their internal environment by using energy to move ions and molecules across their membranes. Protein molecules, embedded in the membrane, are involved in this transport (see also membrane).

Actomycin The two proteins most involved in muscle contraction, actin and myosin, form a complex in which fibres lie side by side. When a supply of energy and calcium ions are present, the fibres slide past (over) each other. They are arranged in the muscle so that when this happens, the muscle contracts.

Acute angle An angle between 0° and 90°.

Adaptation All those characteristics of an animal that improve its chances of survival. All adaptations make an organism suited to a particular environment; for example all those characteristics that make a baboon look the way that it does are helpful in its life on the African savanna and could well be a disadvantage to it if it lived in the jungle.

AIR

very stagnant water

Adenine One of the bases occurring in nucleic acids (DNA or RNA) and which plays a part in coding genetic information (adenine: $C_5H_2N_4NH_2$ or more simply as $C_5H_4N_5$).

rat-tailed maggot

this breathing tube is an adaptation for living in foul water that lacks oxygen

amine group (see amino acid)

Adenosine A nucleotide (building block of nucleic acids) made of adenine and a 5 carbon sugar.

Adiabatic If a bubble of gas rises through the atmosphere, it will cool down as the pressure falls. If there is no transfer of heat into the bubble from the air mass outside, the process is adiabatic. During an adiabatic process, no heat enters or leaves the system.

Adipose tissue Fatty tissue found in the bodies of animals. The cells store the fat in a single large vacuole. Adrenaline and other substances stimulate release of the fat (see also Brown fat).

Adjacent side Of triangles it is that side of the triangle that is next to the angle being discussed. In the triangle on the right, AC is adjacent to angle ø. Side BC is opposite angle ø. The side AB is the hypotenuse

ADP   Adenosine diphosphate is found within cells and is a vital part of the energy cycle that goes on in living organisms (See also ATP).

Adrenal gland   Hormone secreting glands which are found in front of (above, in the case of humans) the kidneys in most amphibians, reptiles, birds and mammals. The glands are able to secrete several different hormones which help to control mineral and sugar levels within the body or which prepare the body for vigorous activity (flight or fight). (see also Adrenaline)

Adrenaline   A hormone released by the inner part of the adrenal glands. It gets the body ready for activity by:
1. increasing the release of stored sugar and fat (from liver and fatty tissue),
2. acting on blood vessels and so causing more blood to flow to the heart and skeletal muscles,
3. increasing the rate and power of the heart beat,
4. improving air flow to and from the lungs,
5. reducing blood supply to skin and intestine.

Aerobic   A process that requires oxygen i.e. dissolved O_2. During **aerobic respiration** energy is transferred from sugars or fats into a form which is more useful to cells (ATP).

Afferent   Leading towards e.g. afferent nerves carry sensory information towards the central nervous system (opposite of efferent).

AIDS   (Acquired immunodeficiency syndrome) A 'new' disease probably caused by Human T leukaemia virus. The disease may take from 5 to 10 years to produce symptoms. These symptoms include an unusual type of skin cancer (Karposi's sarcomas), and a whole range of infections that occur because the person's immune system has been damaged e.g. thrush, severe diarrhoea, brain infections, pneumonia etc.AIDs is now known to affect both heterosexuals and homosexuals (see also HIV).

Agar   Jelly like substance that is extracted from certain seaweeds. It is composed of a mixture of polysaccharides.

Albumins   Small proteins which make up about half of the human plasma protein content. They are made by the liver and are important as carriers of fatty acids and in maintaining the bloods osmotic pressure. Also found in egg white.

Alcohols   Organic molecules which have one or more –OH groups attached directly to carbon atoms, e.g. ethanol (C_2H_5OH) Many alcohols are poisonous, common alcohol (ethanol) being no exception, which is why people can suffer hang-overs.

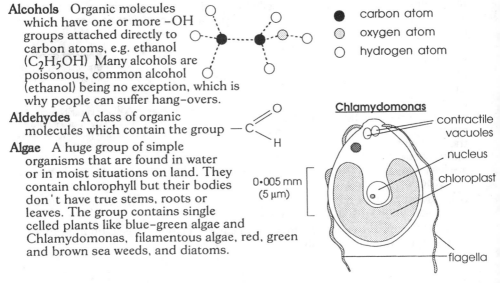

● carbon atom
◎ oxygen atom
○ hydrogen atom

Aldehydes   A class of organic molecules which contain the group

Algae   A huge group of simple organisms that are found in water or in moist situations on land. They contain chlorophyll but their bodies don't have true stems, roots or leaves. The group contains single celled plants like blue-green algae and Chlamydomonas, filamentous algae, red, green and brown sea weeds, and diatoms.

Chlamydomonas

contractile vacuoles
nucleus
chloroplast

0·005 mm
(5 μm)

flagella

Alimentary canal   A tube designed for processing and absorbing food and water. In some animals it has only one opening e.g. sea anemone, but in most animals there is a mouth at one end and an anus at the other e.g. earthworms, birds, aardvarks. The diagram on the right shows the main parts of the tract in humans (including some of the nearby organs) see your own notes for more details.

Alkali   An alkali will react with an acid to form a salt. An alkali is a soluble base. An alkaline solution always has a pH greater than 7.

Alkali metals   The Group 1 metals i.e. lithium, sodium, potassium, rubidium, caesium and francium. These are all very reactive and form ions with one positive charge e.g. Na^+.

Alkaline earth metals   The elements in Group 2 i.e. beryllium, magnesium, calcium, strontium, barium and radium. They all have combining power 2 and form ions with two positive charges e.g. Mg^{2+}.

Alkaloid   A group of organic substances found in some plants e.g. codeine, cocaine, nicotine, morphine, strychnine, quinine. Many have a medical use.

Diagram labels: oesophagus (gullet), trachea (wind pipe), heart, lungs, liver, pancreas, kidney (behind the intestine), gall bladder, stomach, spleen, large intestine, small intestine, rectum

Alkane   Another name for members of the group of organic compounds known as paraffins. Methane, ethane, propane and butane are gases at room temperature, the others are oils or solids. They have the general formula C_nH_{2n+2}.

Allele   Simply stated, alleles are the different forms of a particular gene. Any of the alleles controlling a characteristic (e.g. flower colour in peas) will occur at the same place on the chromosome (i.e. at a particular **locus**).

Allotrope   Some of the elements can exist in two or more forms which are physically different but are chemically identical. E.g. oxygen can exist as ozone (O_3) or as the normal diatomic oxygen (O_2), carbon can exist as graphite or diamond, sulphur can exist as two types of crystals and as plastic sulphur.

Alloy   This is a mixture of two or more metals e.g. bronze is a mixture mainly of copper and tin.

Alloys are often stronger than the metals from which they are made. In crystals of pure metal, the layers of atoms are so regularly arranged that they will slide over each other fairly easily. By mixing different metals (with their different sized atoms) the layers are less regular and therefore it is not as easy to sheer them (slide one layer over the other).

slipping happens easily along these layers in the crystal

the impurity atoms in an alloy make it harder for the layers to slide over each other

Alluvial   Material that has been deposited by rivers. Usually the term is used for silt or soil. Alluvial soils are usually very fertile.

Alnico   Alloys used to make permanent magnets. They are based on iron, nickel, aluminium, cobalt and copper.

Alpha particle   These seem to be the same as fast moving helium nuclei (He^{2+}). They travel only a few centimetres in air and are stopped by thick paper. When an atom gives off an alpha particle, its nucleus has lost 2 protons (and 2 neutrons) and so it has changed to an atom of a different element two places down the periodic table e.g. radium gives off an alpha particle and decays to radon.

$$ {}^{226}_{88}Ra \longrightarrow {}^{222}_{86}Rn + {}^{4}_{2}He $$

mass number of the radium atom

atomic numbers (the number of protons)

Alternating current   Both the size and the direction of the current keep changing. The rate at which the changes take place can be varied. The AC in the mains changes direction 100 times each second, that is, it travels in a particular direction 50 times a second (frequency = 50 Hz). The size of the current and voltage keep changing and so "average" values (**Root Mean Square, R.M.S.,**) or maximum values (**Peak**) are used. To get from R.M.S. to peak voltage, multiply the R.M.S. voltage by 1·4142 . (1·4142 ≈ square root of two)

Graph showing how voltage can change as time passes

R.M.S. voltage

peak voltage

Changing voltage (V)

Time (sec.)

Alternative energy   Energy sources which are renewable e.g. wind, tidal or solar power.

Alternator   A generator that produces alternating current.

Alum (e.g. potash alum)   Aluminium potassium sulphate $(K_2SO_4Al_2(SO_4)_3.24H_2O)$.
Alums have the general formula: $(M^+)_2SO_4. M^{3+}(SO_4)_3 . xH_2O$ (M: metal ion)

Alveolus   Minute air-filled sacs that occur in clusters at the ends of bronchioles in the lungs of vertebrates.The surface in contact with the air is kept moist with a liquid which lowers the surface tension. Alveoli have a very good blood supply which is important as they are the place where exchange of oxygen and carbon dioxide to and from the blood takes place.

Amalgam   An alloy of mercury.

Amplitude modulation (AM)   One of the main methods of sending radio information.

carrier wave before modulation

signal to be transmitted

signal which arrives at our radio

Ambient   Surrounding, as in 'ambient temperature',   i.e. the temperature of the air around us.

Amino acid   These are the basic building blocks of protein molecules. **Proteins** are long chains of amino acids joined by a particular type of bond. Although there may be several thousand amino acids in each molecule of protein there are only about 20 different types of amino acid found in living organisms.

Each different amino acid will have hydrogen or different groups of atoms joined to this place

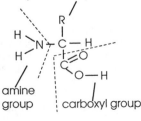

amine group

carboxyl group

Ammeter   Used to measure current in a circuit (i.e. the rate at which charge is passing a point). Most ammeters work by detecting the size of the magnetic effect of the current being measured.

Ammonia A colourless gas with a very pungent smell. It is very soluble in water. $\boxed{NH_3}$

Ammonium The term used for the ammonium ion, NH_4^+. It has a combining power of 1 as shown by the formula for ammonium chloride, $\boxed{NH_4^+}$ NH_4Cl.

Amorphous Having no definite form or shape as in the powdery **amorphous sulphur**.

Amp hour (ampere hour) This is a practical unit of electric charge. It is one amp flowing for an hour i.e. 3600 coulombs. Batteries are often rated in amp hours so that a 40 amp hour battery (as found in cars) should deliver 1 amp for 40 hours, 4 amps for   10 hours and so on. This relationship begins to break down with very large currents in that, the battery would not be able to supply a steady 20amps for a full 2 hours.

Ampere A unit of current. The current is 1 ampere when 1 coulomb passes a point every second. Symbol: A

Amphetamine The amphetamines have a stimulating effect on the central nervous system and so were once thought to be useful in the treatment of depression. It was found to be strongly addictive and so is not much used in medicine now. (Amphetamine: $C_6H_5CH_2CHNH_2CH_3$ Trade name : Benzedrine)

Amplitude In the case of a pendulum, the amplitude is half the length of one swing, i.e. in waves it is the distance from the resting point to a crest (or a trough). Amplitude gives us an idea of how much energy the waves are carrying.

Amylase Any enzyme that is capable of splitting starch or glycogen into sugars. Amylases are found in plants and animals e.g. there are amylases in germinating seeds where they make the stored starch available to the growing embryo. They are also found in saliva, in pancreatic juice and the liver.

Anabolism Anabolism is going on more obviously in young bodies. It is the process by which complex materials are built up from simpler molecules in tissues e.g. anabolism occurs when muscle, bone, fat, skin etc are being produced during growth of the body. **Anabolic steroids** (e.g. testosterone) speed up this process and so are sometimes used by athletes to encourage the deposition of muscle. One side-effect produced is an increase in aggression and this personality change often persists for some time after the athlete has stopped taking the drug.

Anaerobic Without free oxygen. Usually both plants and animals have to use oxygen when making energy available to their tissues (i.e. during cell respiration) but when there is no oxygen most can respire anaerobically for a while. Commonly, anaerobic respiration produces ethanol in plants and lactic acid in animals and as these are both toxic at high concentrations, anaerobic respiration is often only a short term solution to energy needs. Organisms that live in the gaps between our teeth, in our intestines, in polluted water, in thick mud or other such places have to be able to get by without oxygen and so must respire anaerobically.

Analgesic A substance (or mixture) which reduces our awareness of pain e.g. aspirin, paracetamol or, at the other end of the scale, morphine. In some cases it may not be clever to take an analgesic e.g. if we have a sore back it may be better to use that pain to show us what we can and can't do. If we deaden the pain we may ignore the warning pain and so add to the damage.

Analog signal We can transmit or record information e.g. sound, in the form of smooth variations in voltage so that a large voltage represents the strong part of the signal. Tiny voltages for weak signals.(We describe these as analog signals), A real problem with analog signals is that if, for some reason, we lose strength of the signal (usually from the peaks and troughs), these errors will be passed on. This doesn't happen as readily with digital signals.

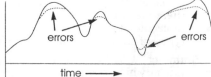

Analogy A comparison drawn between two separate events or sets of circumstance. In science we may use an analogy to clarify a particular point. For example we might try to explain what is going on in an electric circuit which contains an ammeter, voltmeter, on/off switch, and an electric motor, by building a water circuit with a flow meter, pressure gauge, valve and water turbine.

Anaphase A stage in cell division during which the chromatids separate and move apart to the poles.

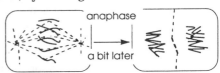

AND gate In a circuit with an AND gate, a current will only flow when there is a voltage at both A and B.

Androgen Male sex hormone e.g. testosterone.

Anechoic An anechoic chamber has its walls covered with absorptive material so that there is almost no reverberation. Any sounds made in the chamber are almost totally absorbed by the walls. Small reflective pyramids are used to break up any standing waves.

Anemometer An instrument used to measure the windspeed.

Angle of rotation Pretty obvious really, it is the angle through which an object rotates. It is useful when we are working out the rate at which an object is spinning (its angular velocity) or the momentum of spinning bodies (angular momentum). Suitable units for angular velocity: degrees per second (or radians per second).

Angstrom A ten thousand millionth of a metre 10^{10} m . The unit is not part of the SI system.   (Symbol: Å)

Angular momentum This gives us a measure of how difficult it will be to slow down a spinning object.

Angular velocity The rate at which an object rotates about its axis.

Anhydrous Without water e.g. anhydrous copper sulphate is copper sulphate without its water of crystallisation. It is a white powder rather than the blue crystals.

Anion Anions carry negative charge and will move to the anode during electrolysis. They may be single charged atoms (Cl) or groups of charged atoms (NO_3^-, CO_3^{2-}, SO_4^{2-} etc.).

Annealing Metal or glass objects may have stresses within them which make them likely to crack or shatter and these can often be reduced by heating up the piece and then allowing it to cool very slowly. This process is called annealing.

Annual ring Woody plants (shrubs, bushes or trees) lay down new growth during the warmer parts of the year. The type of growth changes slightly from spring to autumn and so the bands of growth are usually quite easily visible. This is most noticeable in those parts of the world with an obvious summer and winter (i.e. parts away from the tropics). (see also dendrochronology).

Details of a small section of woody stem

annual ring
smaller vessels of autumn wood
larger vessels of spring wood

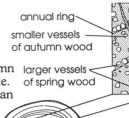

Anode Positive electrode. During electrolysis it is the anode that attracts negatively charged ions (hence, anions). In a disposable battery it is the electrode that becomes positively charge. There is also an anode in radio valves (see thermions).

these rings may have been laid down during years with poor rainfall or very cold summers.

1 cm
Cross section of 11 year old stem

Anodising We can protect certain metals (e.g. aluminium) by using electrolysis to coat their surface with a layer of oxide. During this process the metal object is the anode in the electrolytic bath. An added advantage is that the oxide layer will often strongly absorb coloured dyes.

Antacid Substances that can counteract acidity in the stomach. They are used to treat the symptoms of heartburn (caused when acid from the stomach rises into the oesophagus). Aluminium hydroxide, magnesium oxide or calcium carbonate are often used.

Anthracite Anthracite contains much more carbon than coal . It is 92–98% carbon. It also contains much less of the oily substances found in coal (oils and tars).

Anthropomorphic Giving human characteristics to non–humans, usually to animals e.g. To say that bloodhounds must be such sad animals because of their lined and drooping faces and also that it must be horrible to be an earthworm, having to live in that cold damp soil which is in fact their normal environment.

Antibiotic These substances are capable of killing bacteria or fungi or slowing down their growth rate. They are therefore very useful in controlling disease. They were first discovered in fungi and bacteria but many different microorganisms make them as a way of protecting their space from other microorganisms. Most medical antibiotics are now produced synthetically. Antibiotics are very powerful tools in medicine but have very little effect on viruses and so cannot cure the common cold, poliomyelitis or AIDS.

Antibody Proteins which can react with, and so inactivate, harmful molecules. By making antibodies vertebrates are able to cure themselves of infections caused by viruses (flu, measles, mumps etc.), bacteria (typhoid, cholera etc.), or parasites (malaria). Antibodies are not successful against every type of infection. They are produced by some white blood cells.

Anticline A dome-shaped folding of the rock strata. It may be like a ridge or an upside-down saucer.

Antidote A substance that counteracts the effect of a poison.

Antifreeze As the name indicates, these substances prevent the formation of ice crystals. Many plants, some insects and some fish contain natural antifreezes to help prevent the damage to their cells that would occur if ice crystals were able to grow through the cell membranes, puncturing them. Ethylene glycol is a common antifreeze used in motor car radiators.

Antigen These are proteins or carbohydrates that are foreign to a particular organism i.e. they are not produced by that organism. Examples include the pollen that causes hay fever, mosquito saliva proteins that cause the itchy bumps at the site of the bite , the virus that causes mumps or the bacterium that causes tuberculosis. Antigens stimulate the production of antibodies.

Antihistamine A substance which can make us drowsy. The main effect is to prevent the itchiness that can occur during an allergic reaction such as occurs after insect bites.

Antimatter Antimatter has never been demonstrated in the universe but it is theoretically possible. If antimatter were to meet its matter counterpart the result would be the annihilation of both, e.g. if atoms of hydrogen and antihydrogen collide there would be annihilation of both.

Antioxidant These slow down oxidation. It is oxidation of fats that make foods taste stale and so antioxidants are often added to processed food to increase shelf life. They are also added to petrol, rubber, many plastics and paints.

Antiseptic A substance that **kills microorganisms**, or slows down their growth. Antiseptics do not damage human tissue (unlike disinfectants which are much harsher).

Aperture An opening. The aperture of the human eye is known as the **pupil**.

Appendage An appendage is something added to the main part. In biology an appendage can be a limb or wing or other outgrowths from the body.

Approximation An assessment that is nearly accurate. We may not have time to count all the mature elms in the wood and so we are forced to make an approximation. Life being the compromise that it is, we are regularly called upon to make approximations e.g. writing the essay will take 3 hours, getting to Norwich will take about 7 hours.

Aqueous In water. E.g. 'an aqueous solution of potassium nitrate'.

Arc Part of a curve.

Archimedes' principle When an object is lowered into a liquid it appears to lose weight. The weight lost is equal to the weight of the liquid displaced. A balloon in air will also appear to lose weight. The weight lost in this case is equal to the weight of the air displaced by the balloon's shape.

Arbitrary Based on personal whim. Arbitrary units on the axes of a graph may be chosen arbitrarily i.e. they are there to give some sense of scale but do not relate directly to the values plotted.

Potential difference (V), vertical axis marked + 3 2 1 0 1 2 − 3; horizontal axis time (arbitrary units) marked 2 4 6 8 10 12 14 16, showing a wave.

Arithmetic mean To calculate the arithmetic mean we add all the values together and then divide by the number of values.

Arithmetic sequence A sequence of numbers that is produced by adding the same number each time e.g. adding 4 to get 7, 11, 15, 19, 23, 27 . . . . The number that is added is called the constant, or the common difference.

Artery Tubes in the vertebrate body that carry blood. They have thick walls and a regular circular shape when seen in cross section. They have no valves except in the heart itself. They carry blood away from the heart. **Not all arteries carry oxygenated blood.** (the pulmonary artery carries deoxygenated blood to the lungs). Blood flows quickly through arteries and it flows in surges.

Artifact An object made by people at some stage in our history e.g. stone arrowheads or pottery.

Asbestos A fibrous mineral which is very resistant to heat and so has been widely used as a lagging for pipes and boilers and as insulation. Some types of asbestos can induce a form of cancer in the pleural space. There is at present no cure for this form of cancer. Asbestos continued to be used long after all this was known and many people throughout the world now have asbestos in their lungs and pleural cavities. Insurance claims for the damage could well end up crippling many insurance companies.

Ascorbic acid Vitamin C. It is essential for the healing of wounds and during the synthesis of the protein collagen, so important in the structure of bones. We get ours from plants.

–ase A suffix used to form the names of many enzymes as in protease, an enzyme that digests protein, lipase, an enzyme that digests lipids.

Aseptic Free from bacteria and other microorganisms or their spores.

plant leaf

Asexual reproduction   No **fertilisation** is needed for this. Plants can reproduce themselves from tubers, bulbs, creeping roots or spores. Very simple animals just divide in two (as happens in the case of unicellular pond organisms) or bud another of themselves from their bodies as happens in Hydra (a small organism found in fresh water). The main point   the parent is budding is that **only one parent is ever involved** and the   off another Hydra.   tentacles used offspring are genetically identical, they are **clones**   to catch prey of the parent.

Aspirin   A substance which acts as a painkiller (analgesic) and which also reduces fever. It can be quite damaging to the lining of the stomach, causing bleeding. (acetylsalicylic acid: $CH_3COOC_6H_4COOH$) An aspirin-like substance is found in certain plants e.g. meadowsweet or weeping willow.

Assaying   Analysing a mixture to decide the amount of one of the ingredients.

Astable   An electronic switch which keeps changing from on to off and back on again. The switching rate can be varied to several million switches per second. Car indicators are controlled by an astable.

Atmosphere   A unit of pressure. 1 normal atmosphere = 101 325 pascals (1 pascal = 1 newton per square metre)

Atom   This is the smallest part of an element that can take part in a chemical reaction. Almost all the mass of the atom is in the nucleus, the positively charged part at the centre, made of protons and neutrons. When an atom carries no charge there will be as many electrons around the nucleus as there are protons in the nucleus. Chemical reactions occur between atoms because there is sharing or transfer of the outer electrons (chemistry involves the outer electrons).

Atomic lattice   A regular network of atoms, such as may be found in a crystal of pure metal.

Atomic mass   See relative atomic mass.

Atomic number   The number of protons in the nucleus of the atom. The periodic table at the back of the book shows atomic numbers. It is important not to confuse atomic number with **atomic mass**.

Atrophy   A reduction in size which may be caused by starvation, lack of use or may be controlled genetically.

Attometre   One million million millionth of a metre   i.e. 10^{-18}m.

Aurora borealis (Northern lights)   Shimmering lights (usually in reds and greens) in the form of streamers and curtains which can appear over the north and south poles. They are produced when fast moving charged particles from the sun (see **solar wind**) collide with particles in the earth's atmosphere and cause them to glow.

Autoclave   A container in which high pressure steam is used to kill bacteria and fungi and their spores, and to denature viruses.

Autolysis   The breakdown of damaged cells or groups of cells to release simple substances like fatty acids or amino acids. These can then be used again by the organism. Autolysis is essential in any complex organism for otherwise it would become cluttered with non-working cells. Granules in the cytoplasm containing digestive enzymes (**lysosomes**), bring about the digestion.

Autosome   Any chromosome other than a sex chromosome.
                         (sex chromosome = heterosome)

Autotrophic   Green plants and certain bacteria are autotrophs. This means they are organisms that are able to manufacture all the necessary organic compounds from water, carbon dioxide and mineral ions.

Auxins A group of substances which have an effect on plant growth. They cause elongation of cells in stems and roots by stimulating root formation. Plant stems have the ability to grow up and towards the light and their roots grow downwards. Auxins are involved in both of these processes.

Average speed $= \dfrac{\text{Distance travelled}}{\text{Time taken}}$ (suitable units: m/s or m s^{-1})

Avogadro's number This is the number of 'particles' (**ion pairs**, atoms or molecules) in one mole of the substance. For example, 197 grammes of gold contains about 6 x 10^{23} gold atoms. The more accurate value for this number is 6.022045 x 10^{23}. Normally we don't bother to remember constants but this one occurs so often that it is worth learning the first version (i.e. 6 x 10^{23}). Have a look at the relative atomic mass of gold.

Axon The axon is the nerve fibre that carries impulses away from the main part of the cell (containing the nucleus) (see also **neurone**).

Back EMF Electric motors and electric generators are very similar in some ways and so, when an electric motor is made to work i.e. spin, it is also acting like a generator i.e it produces a voltage and a current. This second voltage opposes the voltage that drives the motor i.e. it is a back EMF.

Voltage that makes the motor turn

Reverse voltage produced by the spinning coil.

Background radiation As you read this definition your body is being bombarded by radiation from the world around you. Most of this radiation comes from radioactive materials in the rocks, soil and building materials but a small amount comes from outer space as **cosmic radiation**. The cosmic radiation has very high energy and consists mainly of charged particles e.g. protons.

Bacteriophage A virus that invades bacteria, multiplying inside them and eventually destroying them.

Bacterium These are among the simplest of all known organisms. Only some of them cause disease. The genetic material is not surrounded by a membrane (i.e. they have no obvious nucleus). Bacteria are very important in the recycling of plant and animal matter during decay.

A diagram showing the main features of a bacterium

flagellae

cell wall

granule

cytoplasm

slime layer

membrane

0.5 to 1.5μ m

nucleoid (no membrane around it)

Bad breath (halitosis) Bad breath can have two causes:
1. It can be caused by serious decay in the teeth or by decaying food caught up between the teeth. The smell is collected by the breath as it passes out through the mouth. Gently drawing dental floss though the back teeth can show whether food is collecting there, it has a characteristic smell. Move the floss through in a single pull.

2. It can be caused because substances in the blood diffuse across the lining of the lungs and pass out with the breath. Such bad breath might result after eating very spicy food or garlic. The smell is usually less pleasant than the smell of fresh garlic or spice possibly because the substances have been slightly changed during digestion and in the blood (see also **ketone bodies**).

Baking powder   A powder made from sodium hydrogen carbonate ($NaHCO_3$) and tartaric acid. This will produce bubbles of CO_2 when it is heated or when water is added. The bubbles will be trapped in the dough as it cooks so that the cakes or scones are light and fluffy.

Balanced diet   A healthy diet should contain protein, carbohydrate, some fat, minerals, vitamins and roughage.

Bar   A unit of pressure in the c.g.s. (centimetre, gram, second system) system.   1 bar is equal to 100 000 Pascals.

Bar graph   A graph in which we use the heights of rectangles to represent quantities so that comparison becomes easier.

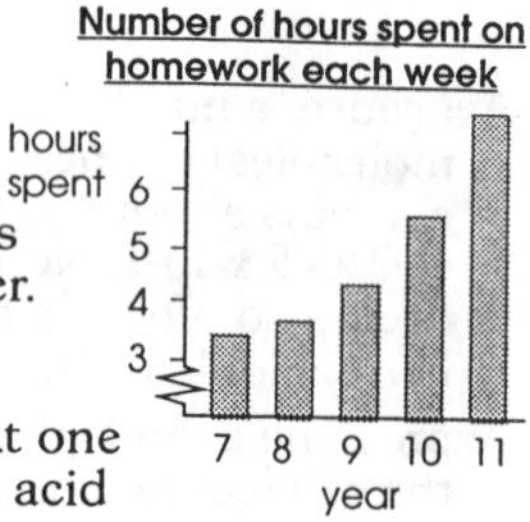

Number of hours spent on homework each week

hours spent

Barbiturates   A group of drugs which have a powerfully depressant effect on the central nervous system (CNS). At one time they were widely used in sleeping tablets. (Barbituric acid $C_4H_4N_2O_3$)

Bark   The outer covering of the stems and roots of woody plants. The general public often think of everything outside the wood as being bark but this is not really correct. Bark is composed of dead cork cells and does not include active **phloem.**

Barn   A unit of area used to measure the cross-section of atomic nuclei, not one of the larger units: 1 barn = 10^{-28} sq. metres.

Basal metabolism   Metabolism : the chemical processes that go on in living organisms. Basal metabolism therefore is the rate of metabolism in the resting organism. It is normally found by measuring the rate of oxygen use when the organism is at rest. It gives the rate at which energy is being used in supplying oxygen and removing carbon dioxide, moving the blood about, and in the gentle repair of tissue that is always going on.

Base   Bases react with acids to form a salt and water only. Bases will neutralise acids. Most bases are insoluble in water (e.g. Copper oxide, Zinc hydroxide). Those bases which do dissolve, will form alkaline solutions i.e. solutions with a pH greater than 7.

Base unit   Base units are not defined in terms of other units. As an example, the metre is now defined as the distance travelled by light in a vacuum in a certain time. The metre is a base unit whereas speed, e.g. number of metres travelled per second, is a derived unit.

Battery   An electric device that uses chemical reactions to produce a current. Strictly speaking, a battery is a collection of cells, linked together in series, but in everyday speech 'battery' and 'cell' are used as though they were the same thing. Each cell will cause a current to flow because of the chemical reactions that go on inside it. The diagram shows a zinc/copper cell: a current flows because the zinc metal atoms change to zinc ions by giving up electrons, these then

some electrical device

Cu rod

Zn rod

dilute sulphuric acid

hydrogen bubbles

At the the copper electrode hydrogen ions are accepting electrons and changing to hydrogen atoms

At the zinc electrode, zinc ions are being formed and the electrons move around the outside circuit.

flow around the outside circuit and back to the copper electrode where they join hydrogen ions, turning them back to hydrogen molecules. Hydrogen is therefore produced at one electrode and zinc is lost from the other.

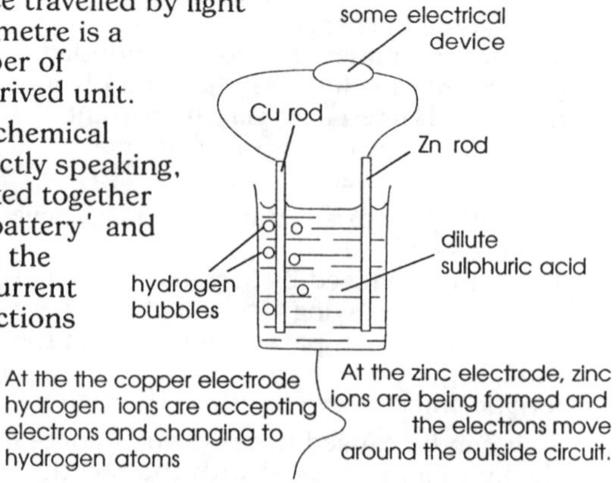

North

Bearings A bearing gives us a way of stating the direction to or from a point. In the case on the right, the bearing of B from A would be 45° (usually this is written as 045°). If B was west of A the angle would be greater than 180°.

Becquerel (Symbol Bq) This is an **SI** unit for the **rate** of radiation.
   1 Becquerel is 1 decay (or event) per second. This is a very small unit.
   1 Curie = 3.7 x 10^{10} Bq . (The Becqueral is a derived unit).

Bel This unit is used to express sound intensities, see decibel.

Benedict's solution This is used as a test for certain sugars. The solution is alkaline and contains sodium carbonate (Na_2CO_3) and copper sulphate ($CuSO_4$).
   Add 2 cm^3 of the solution being tested to a test tube.
   Add an equal volume of Benedict's solution.
   Bring to the boil shaking continuously. If a reducing sugar is present e.g. glucose or sucrose, the solution first turns green, then yellowish and finally, a brick–red precipitate may be formed. (see also Fehling's test).

Benioff zone It is now believed that the lithosphere (the crust of our earth) is made of huge moving **plates**. The parts of the earth where one plate is diving down below another (e.g. in the ocean trenches) are called 'subduction zones' or Benioff zones'.

Benthos Plants and animals that live on the bottom of lakes, rivers or the sea. Benthic animals are found from the high water mark to the deepest parts.

Benzene ring The benzene ring contains 6 carbon atoms arranged in the form of a regular hexagon. The bonds holding the carbon atoms together are slightly unusual which is why they are represented as in the diagram. Benzene is a very nasty substance and is a known cancer inducer. It is present in many types of petrol.

Bernoulli's theorem This describes, in a mathematical way, how pressure in fluids changes when there is a change in speed. At its simplest, when a fluid speeds up there is a drop in pressure and when it slows down there is an increase in pressure. It allows us to explain how aeroplane wings work and how the spin on a ball makes it curve in flight.

Best fit It often happens that when we are drawing a graph, the points do not all fall on a smooth curve or straight line. When this happens we try to draw a line that represents the trend. Do remember that the points on the ends are not more important than any other, many of us make sure that the line passes through these end points but that is wrong.

Beta decay A beta particle is given off from a nucleus because a neutron has changed to a proton. The proton remains in the nucleus and therefore the nucleus gains an extra positive charge and so behaves chemically like the next element up on the periodic table. e.g. radioactive carbon decays to nitrogen by β emission.

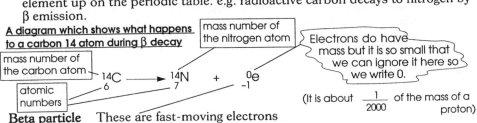

A diagram which shows what happens to a carbon 14 atom during β decay

mass number of the nitrogen atom

mass number of the carbon atom

atomic numbers

$^{14}_{6}C \longrightarrow ^{14}_{7}N + ^{0}_{-1}e$

Electrons do have mass but it is so small that we can ignore it here so we write 0.

(It is about $\frac{1}{2000}$ of the mass of a proton)

Beta particle These are fast-moving electrons and can travel a few metres in air or can pass through a few millimetres of aluminium. They can travel at 90% of the speed of light.

Biased switch A switch which keeps returning to a particular setting, either on or off, e.g. doorbell switches are 'biased on'. Biased switches are also known as monostable switches.

Big bang theory (Superdense theory) This suggests that our Universe has not always existed. It began about 15×10^{-9} (between 10 and 20 thousand million) years ago during a pretty spectacular explosion. At the time of the explosion all the matter in the Universe was concentrated into the space of a single atomic nucleus. In the first 10^{-36} seconds, the basic structure of matter was decided. Within 3 minutes, nuclei of the lighter elements were beginning to form (e.g. helium and lithium). After about 100 000 years after the start, matter and radiation began to separate. The matter grew to form the present stars, planets, galaxies, and background matter. The radiation has spread out to give the background radiation that can be detected today. There is plenty of evidence for the theory but there are also some difficulties.

Bile A secretion from the liver of vertebrates with an important role in the digestion of fats. It is secreted into the small intestine and acts by breaking fats into very tiny droplets (emulsifying them), so making it easier for enzymes to act on them.

Billion British billion is a million million i.e. 10^{12}. The French and Americans consider a billion to be a thousand million i.e. 10^9 and their usage is becoming increasingly common.

Binomial nomenclature This is the method that we now use for naming organisms. It was devised by Linnaeus (a Swedish naturalist living in the 18th century). Every organism is given its own latin name.

Housefly : *Musca domestica* L. or <u>Musca domestica</u> L.

| Common name | genus, always with a capital | species, never with a capital | Abbreviation of the name of the person who first described the organism. Here it is Linnaeus. | It used to be true that the name is either written in italics or underlined. |

Organisms are grouped according to the number of features that they have in common. This means that bats belong with the mammals even though they can fly as do most insects or birds.

Biochemical Oxygen Demand (BOD) A measurement that gives a good idea of the level of organic pollution (as would occur downstream from a sewage outfall). The researcher measures how much oxygen has disappeared from the water in a given time at a certain temperature.

Biochemistry The study of the chemistry of living organisms.

Biodegradable Material that can be broken down by the action of bacteria or fungi. All animal and plant matter, even bone, ivory or ebony is eventually broken down to minerals, carbon dioxide and water. Plastics were the first modern materials which could not be broken down by the action of bacteria, acids or alkalis and this has made them hugely useful, just consider how irksome it would be if your radio rotted just because you left it in a damp cupboard.

Biofuel Fuels like methane produced from sewage or other organic matter, alcohol produced from sugar cane or wood specially grown for burning (e.g. copse willow).

Biogas Burnable gas produced from sewage or other organic matter. This can be produced on a very large scale at sewage works on large dairy farms or it can be done on a small scale to supply villagers with cooking gas from their sewage and vegetable matter.

Biological control   A way of controlling the numbers of pests without using pesticides. Workers try to find the the natural enemies of the pest. Two points are important: the life cycles of the pests must be carefully researched as there have been some costly mistakes made by introducing an unsuitable control organisms and, the control should never be so effective that all the pests are killed. Releasing large numbers of sterilised male insects or using the natural sex-attractants that are released by many female insects to attract males so that they can then be killed are also examples of this type of control.

Biomass   The total quantity of matter in all the organisms (or in a particular species) that inhabit a region, or are found in a population or trophic level.

Biosphere (Ecosphere).   All the living organisms and the physical environment in which they occur. The oceans, the land surface and soil and the lower parts of the earth's atmosphere form the biosphere.

Birth rate   This is usually measured in 'births per 1000 members of the population'.
Human birth rates: e.g.

Kenya,	53 births per 1000 people.
West Germany,	10 births per 1000 people. (figures for 1981)

(birth rate + immigration rate) – (death rate + emigration rate) = change in population

Bistable   This is a switch that is stable in each of two positions, e.g. a light switch can be either on or off.

Bit   One piece of information. In computers it is the amount of information needed to distinguish between 1 and 0 in binary.

Binary   A system of numbers that has only two different digits. These are usually 0 and 1. A comparison between the decimal and binary system is given on the right. The binary system is widely used in computers because the two digits can be represented by a current flowing or by no current.

decimal	Binary
1	0001
2	0010
3	0011
4	0100

Biuret reaction   This is used as a test for proteins (or urea).
Add 2 cm^3 of the protein solution to a test tube.
Add an equal volume of 5% potassium hydroxide solution (KOH) and mix.
A mauve or purple colour develops slowly.   Millon's reagent can also be used to test for protein but it contains mercury salts and so it quite poisonous.

Bivalve   Muscles, clams and shipworms are bivalves. They are molluscs which have quite simple bodies protected by a hinged shell (the shell is in two parts).

Black body   A container that absorbs all the radiation that falls on it. It does not reflect any of it. It is a useful idea in physics but the perfect black body has yet to be built i.e. the black body is a theoretical ideal.

Black hole   An object in space which has such a large gravitational field that neither light not particles of matter can escape from it.   My physics dictionary (The Penguin Dictionary of Physics 1986 reprint) gives the following information 'The enormous gravitational tidal forces inside the black hole draw matter towards the centre where it is destroyed in a region of infinite curvature, a space–time singularity, where the known laws of physics break down'.

Blast furnace   Used for smelting iron. The container is filled with a mixture of iron ore, limestone and coke. The coke is lit at the bottom and fanned with a steady blast of hot air. As the temperature rises, carbon monoxide is produced and this reacts with the iron oxide to give iron and carbon dioxide. The molten iron collects at the bottom. The limestone combines with impurities in the ore producing a molten material known as slag.

Blind spot Simply put, the blind spot is the region on the retina where the optic nerve passes through on its way to the brain. There are no light sensitive cells (rods or cones) in the blind spot and therefore that part of the image does not get to the brain and so cannot be seen. Blind spots are only found in vertebrate eyes where the nerve fibres leave the retina on the lens side , collect together into a nerve and then have to pass through the retina on route to the brain.

Blood A fluid which is responsible for transporting digested food, oxygen, waste products and other smallish molecules (e.g. amino acids, hormones) about the bodies of many animals. In insects the blood moves fairly slowly and transports digested food and waste products but is not used to transport oxygen or carbon dioxide. These gases diffuse in and out of the body along a system of fine tubes (trachea). We could write a book on vertebrate blood and still only scratch the surface but here are some of the main details.

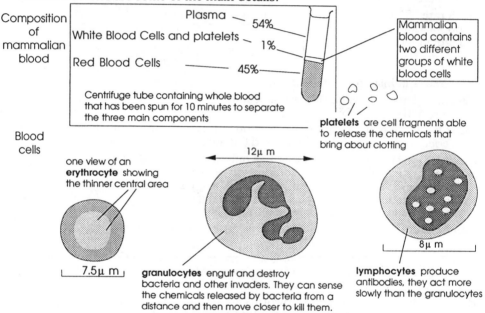

Composition of mammalian blood

Plasma — 54%
White Blood Cells and platelets — 1%
Red Blood Cells — 45%

Centrifuge tube containing whole blood that has been spun for 10 minutes to separate the three main components

Mammalian blood contains two different groups of white blood cells

platelets are cell fragments able to release the chemicals that bring about clotting

Blood cells

one view of an **erythrocyte** showing the thinner central area

7.5μ m

12μ m

granulocytes engulf and destroy bacteria and other invaders. They can sense the chemicals released by bacteria from a distance and then move closer to kill them.

8μ m

lymphocytes produce antibodies, they act more slowly than the granulocytes

Red blood cells - carry oxygen and some CO_2 to and from the tissues and lungs.

White blood cells - There are different types of these, some produce antibodies, others 'eat' (phagocytose) bacteria and cell fragments. This cleaning up by white blood cells is going on all the time.

Platelets - These are fragments of cells, floating in the plasma and responsible for the clotting reaction which causes blood clots to form in wounds.

Blood circulation In vertebrates, blood is pumped about the body through a system of tubes. Although fluid can escape through the walls of the tubes into the tissues, the red blood cells and most of the plasma remain in the tubes so we say it is a 'closed system'.

LUNGS

Everything else

Blood group There are four main blood groups in humans, A, B, AB and O. When certain of the groups are mixed, the red cells clump together (agglutinate). This can cause serious problems when blood transfusions are given. There are **many** other blood groups in humans: The Rh^+ and Rh^- factors can also cause problems during pregnancy in cases where the parents have different groups.

Blood pressure In Mammals blood pressure in the arteries is constantly varying as the heart contracts and relaxes. It is usually measured using an inflatable cuff around the upper arm. For most people this gives changing values between 120 mm (during contraction) and 80 mm (during relaxation). There is, however, no 'correct' blood pressure for people and many people with high pressures can be just as healthy as people who register 120 over 80.

BOD See Biochemical oxygen demand.

Body centred We can pack rows of particles like these ⟶ 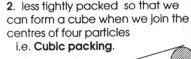 in two different ways:

1. as close as we can get them so that each particle is surrounded by six others which form a hexagon i.e. **Hexagonal close packing**

2. less tightly packed so that we can form a cube when we join the centres of four particles i.e. **Cubic packing.**

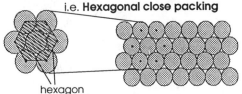

hexagon

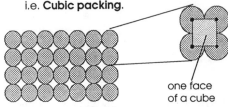

one face of a cube

Boiling point (T_b.) As temperature rises, particles move faster. In liquids there is a temperature at which the speeding particles are bouncing hard enough to break free from their neighbours (overcoming the attractive forces between them). If there are large attractive forces between the particles, the boiling point will be high. When particles break free on a large scale the liquid boils, i.e. bubbles of vapour form within the liquid. Boiling points are affected by pressure. Guidelines:

Relatively low boiling points Substances made of molecules (e.g. methane, CH_4, ethanol, C_2H_5OH).

Relatively high boiling points Substances which exist as giant structures made of atoms or ions.

Bomb calorimeter A strong container used for measuring the energy transfer during chemical reactions. A known mass of substance is burned in the container and the energy released is measured.

Bond The force holding atoms of a molecule or crystal in place. We need to know the differences between three types of bonds; ionic, covalent and metallic.

Ionic bonds (these are also called electrovalent bonds) and the picture below shows a reaction in which ionic bonds form.

sodium + chlorine → **POW** → Sodium chloride

(Na)   (Cl) Na^+(Cl$^-$)

Opposite charges attract and so the positive ions and negative ions are attracted to each other. This attraction forms the ionic bond. The particles in salts are held together by ionic bonds. (continued on the next page)

(continued from the last page)

Methane CH_4 one carbon atom and four hydrogen atoms

Covalent bond In this type of bond, atoms react by sharing some of their outer electrons. No atom has complete control of the shared electrons and so there are no regions with strong positive or negative charge (as there are in ionic compounds). Glucose, carbon dioxide and alcohol are examples of molecules held together by covalent bonds.

Metallic bonds Crystals of metal are composed of positive metal ions held together by a sea of electrons. Many of the electrons are free to move but the metal ions are fixed into fairly regular arrangements typical of crystals. Metal atoms can slip past each other relatively easily but they are then able to form new bonds readily.

Bond energy As an example, propane burns in oxygen to give carbon dioxide and water. Before the molecules can burn they need to be split into atoms. The energy needed to split them into atoms is called **bond energy**. The calculations below show haw we can work out the total bond energy in a mole of propane.

2 carbon-carbon @ 347 kJ mol^{-1}	= 694 kJ mol^{-1}	
8 carbon-hydrogen @ 413 kJ mol^{-1}	= 3304 kJ mol^{-1}	
5 oxygen-oxygen @ 498 kJ mol^{-1}	= 2490 kJ mol^{-1}	
Total	= 6488 kJ mol^{-1}	

Propane (C_3H_8)

Boyle's law Under certain conditions, if we increase the pressure on a gas the volume will decrease in a predictable way.
We can state this fairly formally as follows: At constant temperature, the volume of a given quantity of gas is inversely proportional to the pressure on the gas.

Brain There is a lot we can say about the brain, like about 3 or 4 pages at least, but here we have to keep it short. As a general rule, brains serve the animal by analysing all the sensory information coming in e.g. sight, smell, taste, outside conditions as well as conditions within the body. After analysis, signals leave the brain to muscles or organs so that the animal makes a response in a way that serves its best interests i.e it escapes, attacks, begins chewing etc.

Breakfast cereals This is a personal view. Many breakfast cereals (chocolate-flavoured rice crispies, sugar-coated corn flakes etc.) are really just sweets masquerading as food.

Bronze Alloys made from copper and tin.

Brown fat Cells that are well supplied with blood vessels and nerves and are able to release energy by oxidising fats. They occur in mammals, particularly in the young but also in adults and are very important in raising the body's temperature.

Bubble chamber A device which allows people to view the tracks left by ionising particles. As radiation passes through the tank of liquid hydrogen, trails of bubbles form around the ions produced. These trails can be photographed and analysed. Magnetic or electric fields can be made to pass through the tank and will affect the moving particles giving information about them (see Flemming's left hand rule).

Buffer solution   A solution which is able to resist changes to the pH when small amounts of acids or alkalis are added or when it is diluted. Buffers are very important in biochemistry as many of the reactions studied are sensitive to changes in pH. Blood and other tissue fluids contain buffers.
Example of a buffer: A solution of carbonic acid and sodium hydrogen carbonate.

Building block   Atoms, molecules or ions, i.e. particles that can be joined together to make all the substances we find around us (including the substances inside people).

How on earth can I revise in this light? I really must get a 100 W onion tomorrow.

Bulb   A structure used for asexual reproduction e.g. onion, tulip, or daffodil. Also, device constructed of glass and metal and used in conjunction with electricity, to provide illumination.

Burette   A tube (usually of glass) with a tap at the bottom and graduation marks along its length. Burettes are used to measure volumes of liquids e.g. during titrations. Burettes should be used at the temperature that is marked on their sides when using them with organic mixtures or alcohol.

A Burette

Burning (or combustion)   Substances which are burning are reacting very strongly, usually with oxygen, producing heat, light and flame.

Byte   A sequence of bits in a computer that are processed as one unit of information (see bit and binary).

Caffeine   A substance found in plants that has a strong stimulating effect on the nervous system and the kidneys. It occurs naturally in tea and coffee and is added to many soft drinks (see also alkaloid).

Calculus   A powerful method of solving problems in mathematics. In simple terms it gives us a way of calculating slopes of graphs or areas under the curve accurately.

Calibrating   Graduating an instrument so that it can be used to measure in definite units e.g. metres, centimetres cubed , amperes etc. The burette shown above was probably calibrated so that it measures in cm^3.

Calorie   This a measure of energy. Calorie is not used in science now. Joule is the correct term.   4.1868 joules   =   1 calorie

Calorimeter   An instrument for measuring energy transfers during reactions.

Calvin cycle   A chain of reactions that occur in the green parts of plant cells during photosynthesis.

Calyx   The outer green leaf-like parts of flowers surrounding the petals. i.e. the ring of sepals.

Cancer cell   Cancerous cells continue to divide even when it is not in the organisms best interests to do so. They increase in numbers and can remain as a lump or spread through the body. These groups of cells draw on the nutrients in the body but contribute nothing in return. By your age, most of the cells in your body have stopped growing and should only divide again if there is a need to repair damage.

Capacitor   Capacitors provide a surface onto which electrons (carrying their charge) can be crammed and stored. The larger the surface area, the more electrons can be crammed onto its surface. So too, the higher the voltage, the more electrons can be forced onto the surface. Capacitors can be made with the conducting layer and an insulating layer rolled up together and placed inside a canister.

A roll of tin foil acting as a capacitor (that can be varied)

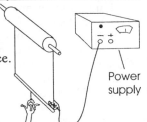

Power supply

Symbols:

fixed   variable   electrolytic

Capillary A tube with a **very** fine hole down the middle. Such tubes are found in living systems: In the stems of plants they are used to conduct water from soil to leaves. In vertebrates they carry the blood from arterioles to veins and, because they have leaky walls, they allow the exchange of ions, smaller molecules and water between blood and tissues (large proteins cannot leave).

Carat A unit of weight used for precious stones, (0·200g). It is also a way of stating the gold content of an alloy. e.g. 18 carat gold has 18 parts of gold to 24 parts of the sample.

Carbohydrate A family of energy providing foods including starch and sugars. These compounds consist of carbon, hydrogen and oxygen (the hydrogen and oxygen atoms are present in the same ratio as in water}. E.g. glucose - $C_6H_{12}O_6$.

Carbon cycle Carbon atoms have been used over and over again since life began about 3000 million years ago. Recycling is essential for life to continue. Simply stated, plants take in carbon from the atmosphere (as CO_2) during photosynthesis. They are then eaten by animals which return the carbon to the atmosphere (as CO_2). Humans now use fossil fuels on such a huge scale that they are raising the levels of CO_2 in the atmosphere.

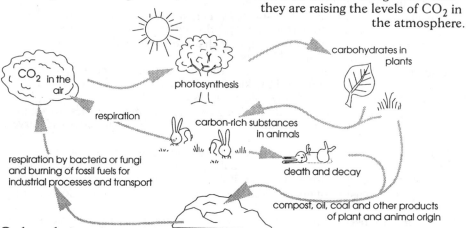

Carbon dating A way of dating natural objects that were produced up to 6000 years ago. A small fraction of the incoming cosmic rays collide with nitrogen atoms in the atmosphere and change them to radioactive carbon (**carbon 14**). This is happening all the time and so a fraction of the earth's CO_2 is radioactive. This same fraction will then be made into plant matter during photosynthesis but, once the plant dies, the proportions of radiocarbon will decrease due to radioactive decay. The older the piece of wood, the smaller its carbon 14 content will be.

Carbon monoxide An oxide of carbon with one oxygen (CO). Each carbon atom is able to react with two oxygens and so carbon monoxide can burn, changing to carbon dioxide and transferring energy. **Carbon monoxide is very poisonous** when breathed in as it combines with haemoglobin in the blood and stops it carrying oxygen. The animal dies from oxygen starvation even though the lungs are working well and there is plenty of oxygen for it to breath. ·

Carcinogen Any substance or physical event (e.g. radiation) that has been shown to induce cancer. If you expose yourself to a carcinogen it does not follow that you will get cancer, but you will increase your chances of getting it. Ultraviolet and X–rays, benzene, mustard gas and thousands of other substances have been shown to be carcinogenic.

Cardinal number The numbers we use for counting i.e. the whole numbers: 1, 2, etc.

Carnivore An animal that lives almost exclusively on other animals. They are the flesh eaters. Fossil carnivores can be identified as meat eaters from the shape of their teeth, because, as with all creatures, tooth structure gives clues about life-style.

Carotid arteries A pair of arteries that supply the vertebrate's brain with oxygenated blood. They contain sensors for measuring the CO_2 levels in the blood.

Carrier Membranes contain protein molecules which are involved in moving ions and other particles across the cell surface. In the case of nerve cells there are carriers busy pumping sodium ions out and potassium ions in. This pumping requires energy (see also membrane).

Carrier wave A continuous stream of radio waves sent out by a **radio transmitter**. These waves have constant amplitude and frequency. The carrier wave is then modified in tune with the sound waves that are being transmitted (see also amplitude modulation and frequency modulation).

Cartesian co-ordinates A way of describing the exact position of a point. In this case it is the distance of the point from two axes at right angles to each other.

Catabolism Breakdown processes in which enzymes are involved. Digestion and respiration are examples of catabolic processes (see also anabolism).

Catalyst These speed up the rate of a reaction. If a tube of hydrogen is exposed to the air, nothing happens.If a piece of platinum wool is placed at the mouth of the tube, the hydrogen burns with a squeak! The platinum has acted as a catalyst... **it has speeded up the reaction without being affected itself**. Other examples: nickel catalysts are used to convert vegetable oils to margarine, protein catalysts (enzymes), allow organisms to speed up reactions so much that life can take place at room temperature.

Catheter A tube which can be inserted into body spaces and used to drain the space or to pump something into it. Catheters are placed in the bladder to drain urine, in the chest cavity (pleural cavity) in the treatment of a collapsed lung, in the intestine or blood vessels etc.

Cathode Negative electrode in electrolysis and vacuum apparatus. Electrons flow onto the cathode from the power pack or battery.

Cathode ray A ray made of a stream of electrons rushing away from the negative electrode (in a vacuum tube). (see also cells and electrolysis)

Cathode

Screen with slit.
The slit will allow a beam of cathode rays to pass.

Anode

Cathode rays zooming down the tube, repelled from the negative cathode and attracted to the positive anode

+

Cation An atom, or group of atoms, which has lost electrons and so is positively charged e.g. Na^+, K^+, Fe^{2+}, Al^{3+}, $(NH_4)^+$. As a general rule, metal atoms become cations, non-metal atoms become anions. During electrolysis the cations travel to the cathode (the negative electrode).

Caudal A word used to indicate that we are referring to the tail, as in 'caudal fin' i.e. the tail fin of fish or 'caudal vertebrae' as found in ox tail stew.

Cell The basic unit of all living organisms. A small amount of living matter, containing a nucleus and other bits and surrounded by a membrane made of fatty substances and protein. Plant cells have a cellulose wall outside the cell membrane. (see also golgi apparatus, mitochondria and endoplasmic reticulum)

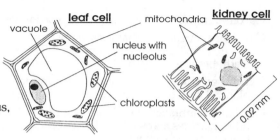

Differences between plant and animal cells

Plant Cells	Animal Cells
Cell wall and a membrane inside the cell wall.	Have a cell membrane but no cell wall.
Cytoplasm contains large vacuoles.	Cytoplasm may have many, very small vacuoles (called vesicles).
Chloroplasts are present in leaf and some stem cells.	There are no chloroplasts, and . . .
Cytoplasm may be seen to be moving around the cell (streaming).	there is usually no cytoplasmic streaming.

Cellulose A fibrous substance made from many glucose molecules joined to make long chains (polysaccharide). It is a very important structural part of plant cell walls.

Celsius See **centigrade** 3 entries further down.

Cement The cement we mix to make bricklaying mortar or concrete is made by heating limestone and clay in a kiln to 1700°C, Gypsum is added and it is ground to a very fine powder. When water is added to this mixture, reactions occur which make it set into a very durable mass. Wet cement is very alkaline and great care is needed when using it as it **will damage skin**. I've spent some time in hospital with a man who needed extensive skin grafts below the knees because he didn't use wellingtons while laying foundations and allowed his jeans to become soaked with cement.

Census An official numbering of the population. In Britain a census is taken every 10 years.

Centigrade A temperature scale in which the melting point of ice was taken as $0°$ and the boiling point of water was taken as $100°$. The units of both the celsius and kelvin scales are the same size but $0 K = -273·15 °C$. (no ° needed for Kelvin)

Central nervous system (CNS) The brain and spinal column.

Centripetal force This is the force that causes objects to move along a circular path i.e. it is the force that keeps accelerating the object towards the centre.

$$\text{Centripetal acceleration} = \frac{v^2}{\text{radius}}$$

Centripetal forces are needed to keep cars turning around corners, balls on string swinging around your head, etc.. We can calculate the size of the force if we know the mass and the acceleration by using $F = ma$.

$$\text{Centripetal force} = m\frac{v^2}{r}$$

Cephalopod Squid, octopus etc. The most advanced group of molluscs. They have excellent vision and a well developed brain.

Certainty When an event is certain it has a probability of 1.

Chain reaction The term is often applied to the chain reaction that takes place inside the core of nuclear reactors, but it can be used for any reaction which keeps itself going because of energy or particles released in the reaction (see also critical mass).

Change of phase When we change a substance from, for example, solid to liquid, there has been a change of phase. Matter can exist in different physical states (solid, liquid or gas) and these are referred to as phases. Unfortunately people also talk about oil and water as separate phases even though both are liquids (see also phase).

Characteristic (genetics) The characteristics of an organism are all those features that allow us to distinguish it from any other organism i.e. all its external features, all the biochemistry that allow it work. In the case of a runner bean plant the flower colour would be a characteristic as would average height or number of beans per pod. At this level we normally stick to characteristics that are controlled by a single gene.

Charge This is one of the properties of electrons and protons that allows them to exert force on each other. The natural unit of negative charge is the charge on the electron. A proton has an equal amount of positive charge. Unlike charges attract, like charges repel. Unit: coulomb.

A coulomb is the amount of charge found on 6.24×10^{18} electrons. Symbol: Q.

$$\text{Useful equation} \quad Q = I\,t$$

Charge (in coulombs) — Q
Current (in amps) — I
Time (in seconds) — t

Charging This is what we do to batteries when they are flat. During charging, energy is transferred from electrical current to chemicals because of changes that happen to the electrodes and solution (see also electrolyte).

Charles's law At constant pressure the volume of a mass of gas is directly proportional to the absolute temperature. This is a fairly formal statement which means that pressure of a gas rises as the temperature rises. **Provided that we use the absolute temperature scale**, the temperature and pressure rise or fall by the same proportion during any change (see also Boyle's law).

Chemical bond see Bond .

Chemical formula This shorthand takes less time to write and gives more information than is given by writing the names in full.

Sodium sulphate

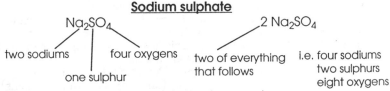

Na_2SO_4

two sodiums | four oxygens
one sulphur

$2\,Na_2SO_4$

two of everything that follows — i.e. four sodiums, two sulphurs, eight oxygens

Chemical interaction Another way of saying 'chemical reaction'.

Chemical reaction Before they can react, molecules, atoms or ions have to bump into each other and the collision must be hard enough to bring about bond breaking. At room temperature only a small fraction of the collisions which take place are violent enough to bring about a reaction. To speed up reactions, we must make the particles collide more vigorously and more often (i.e. we must make sure that lots of the particles have the necessary activation energy) (see also activation energy, bond).

Chip A minute piece of semiconductor containing an electric circuit. For all but the most complicated circuits, the chip measures about 2 mm square by 0.25mm thick. Most of what we see on the outside is the packaging helping to make the chip easier to handle.

Chlorophylls Green pigments in plants which are essential for **photosynthesis**. Chlorophylls transfer red and blue light to chemical energy. This chemical energy is then used to split water and carbon dioxide so that they can be recombined as sugars. The first sugar to appear is usually glucose. In most plants photosynthesis occurs in specialised parts of the cell i.e. chloroplasts.

A diagram showing the main features of a chloroplast

starch granules   chloroplast DNA

grana containing chlorophyll

lipid droplets

ribosomes

0·01 mm

Chloroplast These are organelles within the cytoplasm of many plant cells. Photosynthesis occurs in them.

Cholesterol A compound alcohol which is found in all animal and some plant tissue. It is an important part of animal cell membranes. There is a link between high plasma cholesterol levels and arterial degeneration and so we are advised to reduce the amount of cholesterol in our diets.

Chromatography A technique used to separate substances in a mixture. You may have used it to separate the colours in black ink. The beauty of chromatography for biologists is that it works with very tiny samples e.g. a mm^3 of insect 'blood' would be more than enough.

Chromosomes Thread-shaped bodies, consisting mainly of DNA and protein, which occur in the nucleus of every animal and plant cell. They usually occur in pairs, each member of the pair is said to be ' homologous'. Chromosomes carry the **genetic information**. Heterosome = sex chromosome; Autosome = the other chromosomes.

Class One of the groups used in our taxanomic system. Mammals belong to the class Mammalia, insects belong to the class Insecta. A class contains fewer members than a phylum but more members than an order.

Classification People need classification systems to help them sort out the bewildering array of chemicals, elements and organisms that surround us. The system, now used in biology, is described as natural, because it uses overall resemblances between the organisms. For example, bats, whales, moles and horses have all been placed with the mammals because of their hairiness and habit of suckling their young. This is seen as being more important than their 'fishiness' (whales) or 'birdiness' (bats).

Three systems in use at present: Periodic table (elements)
Linnaean system (organisms)
Herzsprung–Russell diagram (stars)

Cleavage The period of rapid divisions that occur shortly after **fertilisation** of the egg. It also refers to splitting a crystal.

Cloud–chamber A device which allows us to see the paths of ionising particles e.g. α particles, as a row of droplets of water or alcohol.

CNS Central nervous system i.e. in vertebrates it is the brain and spinal chord.

Co–ordinates See Cartesian co–ordinates.

Coal A fossil fuel. It contains more oily substances than anthracite. Coal is fairly plentiful but burning it releases large amounts of sulphur dioxide which contributes to acid rain. Solid fossil fuels start as peat and follow the sequence peat, lignite, bituminous coal and anthracite.

Coaxial A cable with a central wire and an outer conducting cylinder. Television aerial is usually coaxial cable and is used because this kind of cable can conduct signals with very little energy loss and so most of what is collected at the aerial on the roof gets to the set. (Strictly speaking coaxial cables do not produce external magnetic fields and are not affected by them, they are used for transmitting high frequency signals).

Cocaine This is found in the coca plant. It can be used as a local anaesthetic. In the blood stream it acts as a stimulant of the central nervous system (CNS) but is dangerously habit forming.

Coccus A spherical or globular bacterium e.g. *Streptococcus sp.* a few species of which cause unpleasant infections like boils.

Codon A codon is the bit of the genetic code that specifies a particular amino acid. The whole genetic code determines the order of amino acids in proteins (see genetic code).

Coefficient The easiest way to define this is to give some examples:
   1 In the term 3x, 3 is the coefficient.
   2 In the term $7x^2y$, is the $7x^2$ coefficient of y.

Take the case where tickets cost £3·00. The amount we pay will depend on the number we buy so we can write: Cost = 3 x number of tickets. (3 is the coefficient).

Coelom The main body cavity of the more complicated animals in which the gut is suspended.

Coenzyme Organic molecules which are needed by some enzymes before the enzymes can work. They bind only temporarily with the enzymes.
   (see also co-factor, prosthetic group).

Co-factor A general term for a substance that is essential for enzyme activity. Certain enzymes will not work unless they have formed a complex with their co-factor.

Coherent light A beam of light in which the photons all travel on exactly parallel paths **and** in which peaks travel beside other peaks (in phase) and troughs travel beside other troughs i.e. all the photons are in phase. Laser light is coherent.

Cold fusion Nuclear fusion occurs when lighter atomic nuclei fuse together to form a heavier nucleus e.g. hydrogen nuclei fusing to form helium as happens in our sun. This fusion only happens at the very high temperatures that occur on the sun or in the reactor core. For a while it was hoped that people had found a way of making this happen with simple apparatus and at normal temperatures (hence 'cold fusion') but it hasn't been possible to repeat what seemed like earlier successes. (see also nuclear fusion)

Coleoptera Beetles i.e. insects with the first pair of wings hardened into a protective cover for the posterior pair of wings. They have biting mouth parts.

Colligative properties Physical properties like freezing point, boiling point, osmotic pressure, etc. that are affected by the number of particles in solution and not by their nature. A million dissolved sodium ions will have the same effect on boiling point as a million dissolved glucose molecules.

Colloid Some substances are composed of particles so large, that it is not really correct to say that they can be 'dissolved' in solvents. The slightly cloudy liquid that results when some starch is boiled in water is a colloid. Egg albumen in water is another example of a colloid. Egg white and starch are therefore colloids.

Colon This is the large intestine of vertebrates (shown on the diagram, p.9). It is important because it absorbs water from the faeces. It also contains bacteria which produce Vitamin K (important for blood clotting).

Colour A sensation produced when certain wavelengths reach the retina. The table shows the colours produced by different wavelengths (nm = nanometre: 10^9m). The human eye can detect 130 steps of colour across the spectrum. Many more colours are possible when mixtures of wavelengths reach the retina. Make sure that you understand how final colour is produced when paints are

Colour	Wavelength nm
red	620–740
orange	590 –620
yellow	570–590
blue	440–500
violet	390– 440

mixed (subtractive process) compared with mixing wavelengths (addition process).
Colour mixing by subtraction: Yellow paint reflects red, yellow and green light. It absorbs the other colours. Blue paint reflects green and blue and absorbs the others. Blue and yellow mixed will therefore absorb everything but green.
Colour mixing by addition: Here we produce different colours by mixing red, green or blue in different proportions. (see also primary colours, retina, spectrum)

Combining power Is the number of bonds that an atom or group of atoms can form, e.g. carbon,4; nitrogen, 3; sulphur, 2; chlorine, 1; hydrogen, 1.

Combustion Reaction that produces heat and light, usually with oxygen.

Comet Small heavenly body, moving under the attraction of the sun. As they are moving in a vacuum, their tails do not trail behind them but always point away from the sun. The tail is swept this way by the 'wind' of atomic and sub-atomic particles, that rush outwards from the sun (the solar wind).

Communication Words are useful for exchanging information with others but words are not the only way that we exchange information, we also use body language for example, consider what purpose is served by having eyebrows.

Community All organisms that occupy the same area and interact form a community. Some of the organisms in the community trap energy from sunlight (plants), others feed on plants (herbivores), others feed on other animals (carnivores) and yet others are involved in decay.

Commutative Addition and multiplication are said to be commutative because the order in which you deal with the numbers is not important. For example 9 + 23 gives the same answer as 23 + 9. So too, 14 x 11 = 11 x 14.

Commutator A way of connecting the spinning part of a motor or generator with the outside circuit e.g. spring mounted carbon brushes.

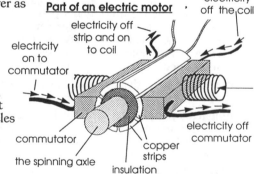

Part of an electric motor

electricity off the coil · electricity off strip and on to coil · electricity on to commutator · commutator · the spinning axle · insulation · copper strips · electricity off commutator

Compass A device that, if used correctly, prevents you walking in circles (or, if that was your wish, allows you to walk in circles with confidence). One end of the needle will always point towards the Earth's magnetic north (provided the needle is free to rotate).

Competition Plants compete for light, carbon dioxide, water, minerals, pollinators and sites for spores or seeds to germinate.
Animals compete for food, mates, breeding sites and shelter from predators.
Competition is usually fiercest between members of the same species.

Compound A pure substance composed of two or more elements which are chemically joined by ionic or covalent bonds. Non-metal compounds contain only non-metal atoms. Methane is a compound of carbon and hydrogen (CH_4). The most dramatic thing about compounds is the huge change in the properties when they form e.g. iron metal reacts with bromine gas to give a green powder. Unfortunately there are many cases where the boundaries between mixtures and compounds are not totally clear so the term is no longer considered to be a very precise one at the university degree level. It is still useful at our level though.

Compression When matter is compressed (put under pressure), its temperature rises and the volume decreases. This effect is most noticeable when gases are compressed e.g. when you pump your tyres and the pump and the tyres warm up. Many reactions take place more readily under pressure which is why there are so many pressure vessels in chemical works.

A slice through a biconcave lens

Concave Curving inwards. A biconcave lens has 2 concave surfaces and is thinnest at the centre and acts as a diverging lens.

Concentration Concentrations are usually measured in grams per cm^3 (g cm.$^{-3}$) or parts per million. Reaction rates can be increased by increasing the concentration of the reactants.

Concentric Having the same centre.

Concrete A building material made from stone, sand, cement and water. A general mix for garden paths: 1 cement, 3 sand and 6 stone. (see also cement).

Condensation reaction Reactions in which a small molecule is given off when molecules join together as happens when glucose molecules join during the formation of starch.

Condenser This apparatus allows you to change vapour back to liquid. Linked to boiling vessel it is useful when separating liquids with different boiling points e.g. alcohol and water.

A glass condenser

water out at the top — cold water in at the bottom

Conductance (conductivity). Wires with high conductance allow electricity to flow along them very easily (such wires have low resistance). Resistance is measured in Ohms so conductance is measured in reciprocal ohms, don't panic! 'reciprocal' just asks you to divide your number into 1.

$$conductance = \frac{1}{resistance} \text{ (in mhos)}$$

drops of condensed liquid

Heat

The unit is the mho because conductance is the reciprocal of resistance (measured in ohms).

Conduction Electrical: This involves the movement of charged particles along a conductor. The conductor could be a gas (as during lightning strikes), a liquid (as in electrolysis) or a solid, like copper wire. The charge carriers could be electrons or ions. (continued on the next page)

Conduction (continued) Thermal: energy is conducted differently through metals and non-metals. In the hot region of a metal, free electrons gain energy; they move faster, and they drift into cooler parts of the metal. There is a drift of electrons with less energy in the opposite direction. These same free electrons are involved in the conduction of electricity, and so it is not really surprising that good electrical conductors are almost always good heat conductors. Most liquids are very poor conductors of energy. The energy is passed on from one particle to the next during collisions so that it moves away from hot regions of the liquid to cooler regions. This usually happens very slowly.

Showing that water is a poor conductor of heat

the water boils at the top of the tube yet the ice does not melt

Ice weighted down with gauze

Conductor If a material allows electricity to flow through it, we call it a conductor, If not, it is an insulator. There is a third group of elements which fit in between conductors and insulators (germanium, selenium and silicon).

Congruent figures Two or more plane figures that have the same size and shape i.e. the shapes can be fitted exactly on top of each other though one may need to be turned over to get it to fit. All corresponding sides and angles must be equal.

Conservation There are quite a few conservation principles, all of which are important but at our level, three are particularly relevant: These are the conservation of mass during chemical reactions and the conservation of momentum during collisions as well as the conservation of energy (energy is always conserved but it may be changed in form).

Constant A quantity that does not vary: The constant pi (π) (the ratio between the circumference and the diameter of a circle) and the speed of light are two examples.

Constellation A number of fixed stars that can be formed into an imaginary group, e.g. the signs of the zodiac. The stars in any constellation may not be close together in space, they just look close together as the stars are all in the same part of the sky.

Consumer You or me, i.e. anyone who uses goods or services. As consumers we all have a responsibility to the planet. We need to be aware of the effect our purchases can have on people of the third world and on our planet.

Continental drift Pretty well as soon as the first maps of the world were produced (1569), people noticed that certain continents fitted together well. Since then evidence which has been mounting for the idea that the continents are large blocks of rock which float on the magma and move slowly about the Earth's surface. People now think that the coal beds in the U.K. and Spitzbergen, which could only have been laid down in hot steamy swamps, were deposited when these countries were much further south. There is also plenty of evidence that Northern Ireland and Scotland were once part of Eastern Canada. At that time an ocean, the Iapetus Ocean, stretched between the rest of Britain and the Canadian mainland. The subject of continental drift goes under the heading of Plate tectonics.

Africa

India

South America

Antarctic

Continuous Data See Data.

Convection During convection, energy is carried through the liquid or gas by bulk flow of individual particles. The fluid gets hot where the heat is being applied, it expands (becomes less dense) and rises taking the energy with it to be replaced by fluid from above.

Converging lens These focus the light that passes through them onto a point. The one shown on the right is a biconvex lens.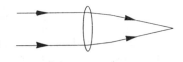

Convex Curving outwards. the concave surface

Coral Corals belong to the same group as sea anemones. They have a skeleton made from calcium salts which may be coloured making it quite attractive in jewellry.

Coriolis' forces Winds moving across the earth follow a curved path over the surface. We expect that anything following a curved path has a force acting on it, hence Coriolis' force (the force used to explain this curved path). The curved paths actually result because the wind is travelling across the surface of a sphere but the idea of Coriolis' force helps with the calculations.

Corn syrup A sugary liquid, rich in glucose, produced from boiled corn starch. The warm starch solution is passed through a column containing a starch–digesting enzyme. The beauty of the system is that the enzyme is fixed to the beads and so is used over and over again (the process is continuous). Less happy is the fact that it allows the developed world to produce a low cost sweetener for confectioneries and so undercuts the world sugar price, causing hardship to the sugar–producing nations.

Corpuscles Red or white blood cells (see blood).

Correlation A relationship between two variables. It can be good or poor. There is a good correlation between working hard and achieving satisfactory results, there is a poor correlation between the annual pilchard catch and the rainfall in northern Slovakia.

Corrosion The process by which metals or alloys are attacked by oxygen, moisture or acids (sometimes by alkalis). As a general rule, corrosion is usually accompanied by the formation of ions.

Cosmic rays Energetic radiation bombarding the Earth from outer space. Cosmic rays are mostly composed of charged particles. Many of them come from the sun. More cosmic rays seem to bombard us from the west than from the east. This is due to the deflection of the particles by the Earth's magnetic field.

Contraceptive pill A hormonal treatment for humans which prevents egg release. In mammals the young remain in the uterus until they are fairly well developed. During this time it is very important that no more eggs are fertilised. Pregnant women manage this by secreting hormones (progesterone and oestrogen) which interfere with egg production. The pill has proved very effective but there can be side effects (weight increase, sensitive breasts, a tendency to nausea as well as a tendency to form unwanted blood clots). This means that many women are unable to get along comfortably with the pill. The search for the perfect contraceptive continues.

Coulomb The SI unit for electric charge. A coulomb is the amount of charge on 6.24×10^{18} electrons. The coulomb is a derived unit and is defined as the amount of charge that passes in one second when the current is one ampere.
    Symbols: C for coulomb,   (Q for charge) (see also charge)

Covalent bond See bond.

CPU Central processing unit of a computer which manipulates information and then provides an appropriate output. It is the 'thinking' part of the system.

Cracking Most crude oil is made up of long chain molecules but the main demand at present is for short chain molecules for petrol. We have worked out a way to 'crack' (catalytic cracking) the larger molecules to make petrols and light oils. If petrol is left for about 6 months many of the small molecules will join together again and vapourise much less readily. This is often the reason why the lawn mower will not start easily in the spring.

Creep The slow yielding of metals or alloys under sustained stress. To emphasise the difference between stress and strain we can say that yield is the strain caused by a stress i.e. the stress is the force, the strain is the movement.

Critical angle The angle of incidence at which the angle of refraction is 90°. There will be total internal reflection once the critical angle is exceeded.

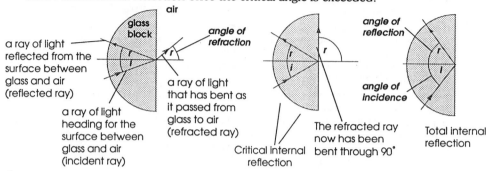

Critical mass This is the smallest mass of material needed to ensure that a nuclear chain reaction is sustainable. If we were adding material bit by bit to a growing lump of ^{235}Uranium, huge amounts of energy would suddenly be released the moment we exceeded the critical mass of uranium. When a uranium nucleus disintegrates neutrons are released. If the mass of uranium is small, these neutrons are likely to leave before they collide with other nuclei and stimulate more disintegrations (a sub-critical mass). Beyond the critical mass the neutrons have far to travel before they escape the lump and so are likely to collide with other nuclei, releasing yet more neutrons which in turn cause yet more disintegrations ... result: **Pow!**

Crystal Crystals are built up from layers of atoms, ions or molecules arranged in a very regular way. Because there are layers, the crystals can be split more easily in some directions than in others (see also body centred).

Curare A substance which causes complete relaxation of the skeletal muscles. It is dangerous because the creature stops breathing (but the heart keeps beating).

Curie If the activity of a lump of radioactive material is 1 Curie there will be 3.7×10^{10} disintegrations each second. The Curie is approximately equal to the radiation from one gramme of radium. Symbol: Ci

Curie temperature If substances are heated, there comes a temperature (the Curie temperature) after which substances will no longer hold on to their magnetism. For iron this is 770°C.

Current (electrical) Whenever charges move, we have an electrical current. This is true whether the charges are positive (e.g. metal ions) or negative (non-metal ions or electrons). We measure current by measuring the amount of charge flowing every second in coulombs per second. Electricity in wires involves electrons flowing. All the rules about electricity (e.g.Flemming's left hand rule) work on the assumption that there is a current flowing from positive to negative.
Symbol: I   Unit: ampere, 1A = (1 coulomb per second).

Cyanide Salts produced with hydrocyanic acid (HCN) e.g. potassium cyanide. Many cyanides are very toxic because they stop the process which makes energy available in cells and tissues.

Cycle   An orderly set of changes that constantly repeats. e.g. the rise and fall of a boat as the waves pass, the boom and bust cycle of lemming population explosions etc.

Cytology   The study of the structure of cells using microscopes. Cytologists try to relate structures to their functions. E.g. see what it is about nerve cells that make them particularly suited to their function.

Cytoplasm   That part of the cell that is outside the nucleus (see also cell).

D.C.   Direct current, i.e. current which flows in one direction. The flow rate may change but the direction is constant (see also alternating current).

DDT   An insecticide that kills on contact and was very widely used until people realised that it was not being broken down i.e. it was accumulating in the soil, in plants and in the bodies of animals and birds. Its use is now restricted in many parts of the world.   DDT : Dichlorodiphenyltrichloroethane.

Dark matter   Scientists have suggested that there is matter, spread through space, which does not give off any radiation and so can't be detected (hence; dark matter). They had to suggest this matter because the mass of the visible universe seems to be too small e.g. some clusters of galaxies, held together by gravity, have too little visible mass to account for the forces needed to keep them together.

Dash pot   A damping device such as is found in car shock absorbers. The car body is attached to a piston that moves in a closed cylinder. The cylinder is attached to the axel. Tiny holes in the piston mean that it can move in or out. The size of the holes will determine how fast it can move.

Data   See continuous or discrete data.

Database   Information stored in a computer in such a way that we can get the computer to sift through it and take out the bits that we are interested in at the time. As an example, a school database may contain the hobbies and interests of all the pupils. If a fashion photographer was going to visit the school to talk about her work the office staff could 'ask' the computer to find everyone who had given fashion, dress making, fabric design, modelling, batik or photography as an interest. It would then have a list of those pupils most likely the be interested. Generally, people must give permission for their details to appear in a data base and they must be allowed to see the information if they wish to do so.

Dating   Finding out the age of minerals or fossils. There are many ways that this can be done (see carbon dating).

Daughter element   An element produced during radioactive decay. In the case of β–decay by carbon, nitrogen is a daughter element :

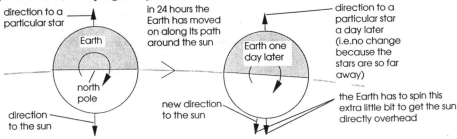

Day length   This should be straight forward, and it would be if the Earth didn't travel around the sun as well as spinning on it's axis. If we judge day length by the stars we get one time, if we judge it by the sun we get another.

Death rate This is usually measured in 'deaths per 1000 people'.
Here are some examples:

Kenya	14 deaths per 1000 per year
West Germany	12 deaths per 1000 per year

Decay That part of the cycle of life in which microbes break down the remains of organisms and release the building blocks. The microbes use some of the substances they digest to make more of themselves but the rest escapes into the environment and so is available to other organisms e.g. plants.

Decibel One decibel represents an increase in the intensity of sound of about 26%. This is the smallest change which the average human ear can detect.
The decibel is not a measure of loudness since the sensitivity of the ear to changes of intensity is different at different frequencies. (loudness is what we measure in our brain)

Deciduous Something which is shed at certain times of the year e.g. leaves of deciduous trees in autumn. Some plants (e.g. certain Eucalyptus species) also have deciduous bark. Mammalian milk teeth are sometimes described as deciduous teeth.

Declination Provided we don't insist on being too precise about our definition, declination is the angle between a suspended magnet and a line to the **geographical north pole**. As the magnetic field inside the earth is constantly, though slowly, changing, there is a steady change in the declination at any place.

Decomposer Without the action of **bacteria** and **fungi** (decomposers), life would not really be possible because all the nutrients would be tied up in the unrotted remains of plants and animals. Although they are a drag in the summer when the fridge breaks down, we would be in serious trouble without microbes (see also decay).

Deficiency disease Diseases caused because some item is missing from the diet (or, in the case of plants, from the soil). E.g. anaemia caused by a shortage of iron in the diet, yellowing in plants caused by a shortage of magnesium in the soil.

Deforestation Trees have been cut down ever since humans had the tools to do so. The U.K. and the rest of Europe were covered with dense forests 3000 years ago, but not so now. In the tropical third world, forests are being cleared to make agricultural land available for the local people (people must have food and so, as populations increase, more land must be found for crops), for attractive timber exported to Europe and elsewhere and for space to raise cattle on a large scale, so that the meat can be exported to the developed world. Cutting down these forests often produces undesirable effects:
1. Once the trees are gone, their roots can no longer send water up into the atmosphere to fall again as rain, i.e. the climate changes, becoming much drier.
2. The vegetation allowed the rain to soak into the soil. Once it is gone, rain floods into the rivers, carrying soil with it as it goes.
3. Tropical forests contain many species of plant which have medical uses, these species are being lost forever.

Demographer Demographers collect statistics on births, deaths, disease and other aspects of human life and then use these to make decisions about the state of communities. Their work is invaluable to planners who need to know what preparations to make e.g. how many hospitals will be needed in 20 years time.

Denature Changes in the structure of large organic molecules (due to high temperatures, unsuitable pH or salt concentration). Proteins or nucleic acids are particularly sensitive to being denatured. In the case of proteins as an example, as we raise the temperature all the atoms begin to vibrate more violently. At some point they are vibrating so fiercely that the molecules are battered out of shape. Changes in appearance of your skin after being burnt are due to the protein having been denatured.

Dendrochronology Dating objects by studying the patterns of annual rings in any wood present (see also annual rings). The thickness of annual rings varies depending on the rainfall and temperatures in any one year. A 5 year drought will show up quite clearly in a slice of timber and will act as a marker for the botanist.

Denitrifying bacteria Soil bacteria that break down nitrates (NO_3^-) and nitrites (NO_2^-) when there is no oxygen present. Nitrogen gas is given off.

Dentine The bony material of which teeth are made. The outer surface of the dentine is covered with enamel. Ivory is mainly dentine.

Deoxyribonucleic acid. There is very good evidence that this large organic molecule contains the genetic information carried by every cell. It is a major component of chromosomes. Genes work by making protein. The DNA carries the code that allows the cells to make the appropriate protein for that time. Once you can relax about large molecules and feel comfortable with the basic ideas of chemistry, the explanation for how genes work is beautifully simple. It is not at all complicated as we once imagined that it might be. (see protein synthesis for a diagram)

Depth of field The distance through the field of view of microscope, camera or binoculars that is in sharp focus. As an example, using a large aperture on a camera reduces the depth of field. This could mean that when we take a portrait of a friend, the eyes might be in sharp focus while the tip of nose and ears are out of focus.

Derived unit A unit that is defined in terms of other units e.g. the unit for work is a derived unit because it uses units for force and distance (see also base unit).

Dermis The inner layer of vertebrate skin (skin is made of epidermis and dermis).

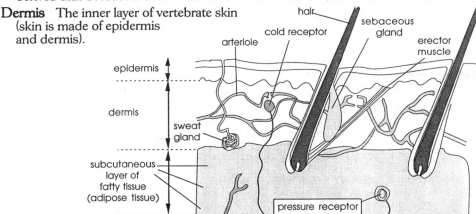

Desalination The process of changing salty water to something that it is suitable for drinking or agriculture. Large amounts of energy are needed for this process and so the final product can be quite expensive even when waste heat from reactors or power stations is used.

Detergent Substances which make fats soluble in water and so are useful for cleaning. Most detergent molecules have one end which dissolves in the fat so that fat droplets become surrounded by detergent molecules. The other ends are water-soluble and so the fat droplets disperse into the water.

Detritus Bits of organic matter such as may accumulate on the forest floor, the bed of a lake, a cave, or the carpet in the lounge. A group of organisms are able to live off such debris and are known as detritus feeders.

Deuterium Hydrogen in which the nucleus contains not just a proton (as in ordinary hydrogen) but a proton and a neutron (heavy hydrogen). Chemically identical to ordinary hydrogen (see also tritium and heavy water).

Dextrose Another name for glucose, the 6-carbon sugar ($C_6H_{12}O_6$).

Dialysis If you were to drop a spoonful of salt into the rice pudding just before the guests arrive, you could rescue the situation by doing something a bit like dialysis. What you might do is to put the salty pudding into a large sieve and then run water over it. The rice is too big to get through the holes but the salt passes out easily. A dialysis membrane is riddled with tiny holes. The holes allow small molecules or ions through but large molecules cannot pass. Using this membrane, the small molecules of urea can be removed from human blood whilst retaining the proteins and blood cells (during kidney dialysis).

blood

Arrows showing the smaller particles moving across the membrane

A solution with most of the salts that are found in blood.

minute holes in the dialysis membrane

Diameter A straight line which runs through the centre of a circle from one side to the other.

Diaphragm 1. The muscular sheet that separates the thorax from the abdominal cavity. It works together with the abdominal muscles to ventilate the lungs.
2. A disc that controls the amount of light passing through it. The iris of the eye is a diaphragm.

Diatoms Single celled algae with a highly textured outer cover made from silica.

Dielectric An insulator e.g. polythene.

Diesel engine An engine that compresses the vapourised fuel so much that it ignites without the need for spark plugs. The engine does not need to have an ignition system but, because of the high compression, it is much more robustly constructed than a petrol engine.

Differentially permeable (DPM) A membrane which will allow some particles through but not others. A dialysis membrane is differentially permeable.

Differentiation. Biology. During this process, cells change from a general type, not really suited to any particular task, to cells which are well suited to the job that they do. Differentiation gives us cells as different as nerve cells, muscle cells, skin cells etc. After wounding tissue, many of the cells there will change back to the basic cell type (they dedifferentiate) and creep about the wound.

Mathematics. A truly elegant technique for getting equations for rates of change e.g. if you have an equation showing how distance from the start is changing with time, you can differentiate it to get a new equation showing how speed is changing as time passes.

There is no magic in involved differentiation Folks ! Just a set of rules to follow

s (i.e. distance) = ut + $\frac{1}{2}$ at^2

becomes: $\frac{ds}{dt}$ (i.e. speed) = u + at

Diffraction Diffraction. Whenever waves pass through an opening smaller than their wavelength they spread out noticeably. this is the sort of spreading that you will have seen on the ripple tank. If there are lots of small opening beside each other (a diffraction grid) , then all the little waves spreading from their separate holes, interact to produce a pattern. The nature of the pattern depends on the spacing of the openings. The spaces between the layers in crystals are about the right space to give patterns when X-rays are shone through them. People have used these patterns to learn about the structure of crystals. Diffraction is very definitely a property of waves and not of moving particles.

Diffusion   The spreading of a substance due to free and random movement of particles. A draught in a room is not an example of diffusion, because in a draught there is mass movement of all the particles.
Even in a house with no draughts, the smell of baking bread soon draws hungry people to the kitchen. These molecules spread through the house because they bounce their way past the other the gas particles. A common mistake is to think that the particles 'want' to move. They move simply because everything in their world is bouncing about. Diffusion is most noticeable in gases and liquids because the particles are free to move about, but it does occur in solids.

Digestion   This takes place in the intestine after every meal. Food substances are broken down to their building blocks for absorption into the blood. The foods that animals eat are too different from their own molecules for them to be able to be used without change. The food molecules are first broken down to amino acids, sugars, fatty acids and so on. They can then be used for repair and growth.

Digital signal   A digital signal is a signal that is made up of numbers. Digital signals are much more reliably transferred, e.g. when re-recording music. Slight differences in the strength of the signal are not important and can be ignored. If the digital recording has been slightly damaged so that the strong blips of current all show small variations, re-recording will make them all the same again. With an analog system, all these slight variations will be passed on to the copy (see also analog signal).

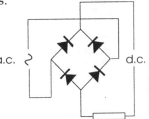

Dilution   Adding solvent so that the solute becomes more spread out. When chemical factories empty their waste into rivers and lakes, they hope that the large volume of water there, will dilute the waste enough to render it harmless.

A full-wave rectifier made with 4 diodes

Diode   An electrical device that allows current to flow only in one direction. A diode can be used to change alternating current to direct current. It won't change D.C. to A.C. though.

a.c.   d.c.

Dioptre   A unit for the power of a lens.

$$\text{Power (in dioptres)} = \frac{1}{\text{focal length (in metres)}}$$

Dioxin   A very toxic organic substance that can cause genetic damage. It is sometimes released when waste chemicals are incinerated carelessly. It is also produced as a bi-product during the manufacture of herbicides.

Diploid cell   A cell in which there are two sets of chromosomes in the nucleus. Most of the cells in the body are diploid. Sex cells (gametes) have only one set of chromosomes i.e. the cells contain only half of the genetic material. Such cells are called haploid.

Dipole   In a dipole there are equal and opposite charges situated very close together. One example of a dipole is given by the water molecule where a slight positive charge occurs on one side and a slight negative charge on the other. This means that when a glass of water is placed between two strongly charged plates all the water molecules will orientate themselves.

a water molecule has a very slight negative charge on the hydrogen side and very slight positive charge on the oxygen side

Diptera The insect group that contains flies with a pair of wings and a pair of tiny modified wings that act as gyrocompasses e.g. bluebottles, houseflies.

Direct current Electric current that flows in one direction. The size of the current may keep changing but the direction is constant (see also alternating current and current).

Disaccharide (Di: two, saccharide: sugar) The sort of sugar that would result when we join two glucose molecules to form maltose. If we join a fructose and a glucose molecule we get sucrose (table sugar).

Discrete data In the case of discrete data it is possible to write down all the data e.g. the numbers of people in a class (e.g. 35, 33, 29, 34) or the numbers of wheels on road transport vehicles (e.g. 4, 6, 10, 12, 16, 18, 20 etc. 4.792 wheels is nonsense). In this it differs from continuous data where every value in the range is possible e.g. we cannot write down every possible sunflower plant height (see continuous data).

Disinfectant Agents used to kill microorganisms and their spores. They are too damaging to use on human tissue and so are used when sterilising toilets etc.

Displacement This is used in physics to mean 'moved'. For example "My tooth suffered a three metre displacement the other day, from my mouth to the dentists bin. Since then the displacement has increased because of the activities of the tooth fairy."

Distillate The liquid that condenses during distillation (see condenser).

Distillation A process for separating mixtures of liquids with different boiling points. It is used to separate the different fractions of crude oil or to purify alcohol in the manufacture of brandy (see condenser).

Diuretic A substance that stimulates the production of urine e.g. coffee, alcohol or substances found in dandelion leaves. The rate of urine production in our bodies is controlled by an antidiuretic that is released from part of the brain and circulates in the blood. It acts on the kidneys reducing urine production.

Diurnal Once every 24 hours.

DNA Deoxyribonucleic acid. There is very good evidence that this large organic molecule contains the genetic information carried by every cell. It is a major component of **chromosomes.** The first thing that happens when a gene begins to work is that a protein is made. The DNA carries the code that allows the cells to make the appropriate protein. (see hydrogen bond for a diagram and see codon and **protein synthesis).**

DNA sequencing Finding the order in which the bases occur along the DNA molecule. People are busy in their labs even now working on the complete sequence of bases in all the human chromosomes. Twenty years ago this type of sequencing was very time consuming and tedious but much of the process has now been automated.

Dominant As the name suggests , certain alleles are expressed even though they are present on only one of the pair of chromosomes. The allele that controls 'tallness' in pea plants is dominant to the dwarf allele. We say that the dwarf allele is recessive (see also allele and recessive).

Doppler effect We hear an example of the doppler effect every time a police car passes with the siren going. The note drops in tone as the car passes. If we consider only the crests of the sound waves and think of a crest heading forwards away from the car. Because the car is moving as well, it catches up a bit before the next crest is released i.e. the wavelength is shorter when heard from the front. People in the car hear a steady note. Doppler shift affects the frequency of both sound and electromagnetic radiation and has many uses: measuring how fast the universe is expanding (red shift) and in radar to decide whether the radar signal is being reflected from a stationary or moving object.

Dormant Sleeping or appearing to sleep. Many organisms have a dormant phase which they use to get through the winter when food is limited. In cold climates plants lie dormant through the winter.

Dosemeter (Dosimeter) A device that is used to measure the amount (of something) received. Dosemeters are most commonly used when working with radioactive materials. One type consists of a strip of photographic film protected from the light. The film is developed after a set time. Radiation will fog the film, the larger the dose, the darker the film.

Double bond Formed when two pairs of electrons are shared i.e. two covalent bonds forming between adjacent atoms. Substances with double bonds are also known as unsaturated i.e. oils are unsaturated fats, lard is a saturated fat (its molecules contain no double bonds).

Dry cell A cell supplying an electric current in which the active salts are dissolved in a paste rather than a liquid. Dry cells leak when the case (which forms one of the electrodes) has been corroded so that a hole appears. There are now small dry cells containing toxic metals like mercury. These are dangerous and should not just be thrown in the bin when used up. Responsible councils will have some system for disposing of these which will work if responsible people dispose of them properly.

Dry ice Solid carbon dioxide. Usually at $-78°C$. Carbon dioxide changes straight from solid to gas without passing through a liquid phase. It is dangerous because it can give very severe frost bite (tissue damage caused when ice crystals grow across cell membranes, breaking them and causing them to leak).

Duodenum The part of the small intestine in which active digestion of food occurs. Absorption of digested food also takes place here. The bile duct and the duct from the pancreas both empty into the duodenum. The lining of the inner surface has many projections (villi) which increase the surface area so speeding up absorption (see alimentary tract).

Dynamic equilibrium A state which gives the appearance of stability but in which there is constant change. The population of the U.K. is said to be stable i.e. the total stays the same even though people are dying and being born every minute i.e. the U.K.'s population is in a state of dynamic equilibrium. This state is very common in science e.g. during reversible chemical reactions, evaporation from a liquid and condensation back to the liquid, or the balance of energy arriving from the sun and being radiated out to space.

Dynamite A useful material which can be used to fracture rocks or shift large amounts of rock (though not always in a controllable way). Dynamite is made from nitroglycerine with other nitrates. These are mixed with wood pulp which acts to absorb the liquid.

Dyne A tiny unit of force i.e. a 10 000th of a Newton i.e 1 dyne = 10^{-4} N

EMF see electromotive force.

E number A system of labelling used in the food industry. The numbers refer to substances that have been added to food e.g. E 110 Sunshine Yellow, E 150 Caramel, E 175 Gold. They are used in the food industry to colour food, help it remain fresh-tasting (e.g. anti-oxidants), keep the mixtures flowing properly through the machines etc.

ER See endoplasmic reticulum.

Ear This organ is able to respond to sound in the range 20 Hz. to 20,000 Hz. i.e. it can hear very low and very high notes, but it gets less sensitive with age and it can be damaged by regular loud noise (loud personal stereos etc.). Ear wax is an antiseptic and lubricant for the drum skin. Simply stated, there are two types of ear wax, hard and soft. Hard wax is more likely to collect in the ears and affect hearing so that it has to be 'syringed' out. Cleaning ears with cotton buds is no longer considered wise as they tend to compact the wax rather than remove it. (see also loudness of sound) Our brain decides how loud a sound is by the number of signals arriving from the cochlea each second. Lots of signals means a loud sound. Different notes stimulate different parts of the cochlea. Low notes are sensed by parts of the cochlea furthest from the round window.

Diagram labels: Semicircular canals (balance); auditory nerve; stapes; incus; malleus; tympanic membrane; oval window; cheap earring; round window; cochlea (senses sound); eustachian tube (connects with throat)

Sound as vibrating air	→	Causes ear drum to vibrate	→	Causes ear bones to vibrate	→	Causes ear fluid in the cochlear to vibrate	→	Stimulates nerve endings

Earth's crust This is the part of the earth we stand on. It is thick below continents, thicker below mountains and thinnest under the sea. The densities of the rocks in the crust are between 2·7 and 3·0 g cm^{-3}. Below the crust is another solid layer, the mantle, with densities of 3·3 g cm^{-3}.

Earthquake There are places on the earth, where one bit of crust slides against another. Most earthquakes start less than 60 km. below the surface. There is a fair amount of juddering (the earth quakes) whenever these rocks slide. The focus is the point where the actual movement took place. The epicentre is the point on the surface where the vibrations were most violent. Three types of shock waves spread out from the focus.
  1. a slow-moving surface wave
  2. a secondary wave which moves a bit faster and is of the transverse type and so will not travel through liquids.
  3. a primary wave which moves fastest of all and which is able to travel through the liquid centre of the earth (it is a longitudinal wave).

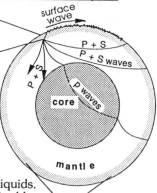

A cross-section of the Earth to show the paths followed by shock waves after an earthquake

Diagram labels: Epicentre of earthquake; surface wave; Focus of quake; P + S; P + S waves; P + S; P waves; core; mantle; crust this is only 25 to 30 km thick (so this diagram is definitely not to scale)

Ecdysis Moulting in insects and other arthropods. A soft new skin is laid down under the old skin, the larger part of the old skin is then digested and reabsorbed through the soft new skin. The creature then raises its blood pressure, splits the old skin and sheds it, climbs out, swallows air to make itself larger and then hardens the new skin.

Echo Usually thought of as sound, reflected back to us from some hard surface (cliff face, sports hall wall, corridor walls etc.). In fact the term is also applied to radar waves (electromagnetic radiation) and shock waves passing through the layers of our Earth.

Ecology This is the study of the way that plants and animals interact with the environment. Ecologists divide up the subject so that they can consider the living components (called biotic) and the non-living components (called abiotic).

Biotic components	Plants Animals	e.g. under climate we might consider: temperature, annual rainfall,
Abiotic components	Soil Climate Topography	windspeed, sunlight intensity, oxygen and carbon dioxide levels, pressure and soil water levels.

Ecosystem Every ecosystem is inhabited by a particular community e.g. woodland community, pond community, tropical rain forest community. An ecosystem is more or less self-sufficient; a collection of organisms in balance with each other and their local environment. Every ecosystem has a source of energy (usually the sun), producers (plants), consumers (animals), decomposers (fungi and bacteria). These are all involved in recycling elements like carbon, nitrogen, sulphur etc..

Eddy currents If metal (or any other conductor) is moved near a magnet, a current will flow. We say "the current is induced". If the material is a loop of wire, then a directional current will result. If the material is a bulky lump, then swirly wasteful currents are produced. These eddy currents cause heating and therefore energy is transferred inefficiently as happens in the metal parts of electric motors and generators. Engineers work hard to find new ways of reducing this inefficient transfer.

Efferent Leading away from. It is applied to nerves, blood vessels etc. (see afferent).

Efficiency The efficiency figure gives us an idea of how effective the machine is at doing useful work. No units are needed because efficiency is a ratio. If I carry a glass of milk up the stairs, the useful work has been done on the glass of milk. My body has also been taken upstairs and so the total work is much greater than the useful work.

Weight of glass of milk: 4 N
Weight of me : 600 N
Height of stairs: 3 m

Useful work = 4 x 3
= 12 J
Total work = 604 x 3
= 1812 J

$$\text{Efficiency of the lift} = \frac{\text{Useful energy transferred.}}{\text{Total energy transferred}} \times 100$$

$$= \frac{12}{1812} \times 100$$

$$= 0.00662\%$$

Elastic collision A collision in which there is no transfer of kinetic energy from the moving particles. Such elastic collisions occur in nuclear physics when particles collide without breaking up. Most of the collisions we meet in everyday life are not elastic i.e. some of the energy in the moving objects appears in another form after the collision e.g. two cars collide, there is a lot of hot, deformed metal, some sparks and the noise of the crash. (see momentum).

Elastin A very elastic fibrous protein that is an important part of ligaments. The fibres are plentiful in lungs and the walls of large arteries. It is one of the very few proteins that is unaffected by boiling.

Electric charge See Charge.

Electric circuit An arrangement of wires, electrical components and a power supply, which is designed to perform a particular task.

Electric current Whenever charge is on the move, there is a current. It does not matter whether the charge is positive (ions) or negative (electrons).
Currents produce **chemical, heating** and **magnetic** effects.

Unit: the ampere (coulomb per second).

Symbol: I. Equations: $P = IV$, $V = IR$, $Q = It$

Electric fields An invisible region around positive or negative charge in which these charges can have an effect on another charge (e.g. attracting or repelling it). Electric fields are what make the hairs on the back of your hand stand up when you bring the charged comb near them.

Electric polarisation Build-up of hydrogen bubbles on one of the electrodes, insulating it from the electrolyte, and so causing the current to fall off.

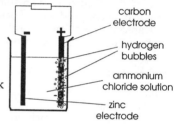

A diagram of a working cell showing hydrogen bubbles building up on the positive electrode

carbon electrode

hydrogen bubbles

ammonium chloride solution

zinc electrode

Electrocardiograph A record of the heart's cycle in terms of the electrical changes taking place second by second in the heart muscles and nerves. The electrodes are taped onto the skin of the chest or back (or abdomen when checking the foetal heart). The technique causes almost no stress as it does not involve injections or cutting i.e. it is non-invasive.

Electrochemical series The amount of energy needed to remove electrons from an atom (i.e. to form ions) differs for different elements. This and other properties of atoms can be used to rank elements in order of reactivity.

Here is a group of metals, placed in order of decreasing chemical activity:

K, Ca, Mg, Al, Zn, Fe, Pb, Cu, Hg, Ag.

Most reactive	This list is not complete, but it does contain more elements than you really need to worry about.	Least reactive

Electrodes The conductors which allow a current to flow to and from the electrolyte or into and from a vacuated space e.g. in a cathode ray tube.
Positive electrode: **anode**. Negative electrode: **cathode**.

Electrolysis Splitting of chemicals into separate components using electricity. For example, copper chloride can be split into copper metal and chlorine gas.

electro lysis
/   /
electricity splitting

Electrolyte Any solution or molten salt that conducts electricity is called an electrolyte. Sea water is an electrolyte as are soft drinks, hydrochloric acid or molten lead bromide.

Electromagnet A temporary magnet made by winding a coil of wire around a piece of soft iron. Large electromagnets are very useful for shifting scrap metal.The discovery of **superconducting** alloys (e.g. niobium-zirconium) has meant that very large currents can now flow with only a small heating effect and so stupendously powerful electromagnets can be made.

Electromagnetic wave Wave–like radiation which carries energy and can undergo interference and diffraction. Electromagnetic waves will pass through a vacuum, which is just as well for us as there is a lot of vacuum between us and the sun and we are totally dependent on sunlight. Energy can also be carried by sound waves, by waves on the water, or shock waves, but these need some substance (a medium) to pass through.

The Electromagnetic Spectrum

gamma rays	X-rays	ultra violet	visible light	infra red	radio waves
very short wavelength (i.e. 10^{-13} m)	10^{-8} m to 10^{-12} m	4×10^{-7} to 10^{-8} m	medium wavelengths (blue 4×10^{-7} m red 7×10^{-7} m)		long wavelength (i.e. 1500 m)

the microwaves used in radar fit in here

Electromotive force (EMF) This is the energy available to produce an electric current in a circuit. If the circuit contains a battery, the EMF will include the energy needed to drive current through the battery itself. The diagrams on the right show a circuit with the switch open and the same circuit with the switch closed so that a current flows. In the top case the voltage across the battery is 6 volts. For our purposes this is the EMF of the battery. In the lower diagram the switch is closed, current is flowing and the voltage has dropped to 5V. The **lost voltage** (1 volt) is the energy needed to drive the current through the battery.

Units of EMF: volts i.e. joules per coulomb.

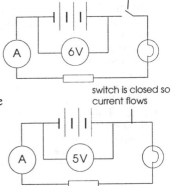

switch is open so no current flows

switch is closed so current flows

Electron The electron carries a negative charge of 1.6022×10^{-19}C. It has a mass of 9.10956×10^{-31} kg. i.e. about one two thousandth of the mass of a hydrogen atom. The electron is one of the basic particles of matter. These fundamental particles cannot be subdivided. (see also elementary particle).

Electron beam Beams of electrons are the basis of television tubes, oscilloscopes, electron microscopes and X-ray tubes. (see cathode ray) .

Electron carrier system Found in organisms, these systems are composed of proteins and co-factors which work together, accepting electrons at a high energy level and passing them on to some acceptor. They are important in photosynthesis and respiration.

Electron microscope A microscope that uses a beam of electrons rather than a beam of light. The electron beam requires a vacuum and so electron microscopes are much bulkier, needing a metal casings, vacuum pumps and high voltages. A light microscope can magnify usefully up to 1500 times, electron microscopes magnify 1 000 000 times.

Electron shells The electrons around an atom's nucleus cannot just be anywhere, they have to occur in certain regions (shells). If energy is transferred to an atom, its electrons will gain energy until there is enough to make them jump outwards to the next shell. As the atom loses energy, the electrons give out their energy as light as they jump back from shell to shell. Very simply, the innermost shell can hold 2 electrons, the next few shells can hold 8 electrons each.

Electroplating Depositing a layer of metal on an object by connecting it to the negative pole of a D.C. power supply and then immersing it in an electrolyte. Electroplating is used to make metal objects last longer or look prettier or both. For good results the process needs to take place slowly and the temperature must be controlled.

Electroscope A devise for detecting electric charge. In the case of the gold leaf electroscope, when both gold leaf and the metal bar carry the same strong charge they repel and the gold leaf swings away from the bar.

Elementary particle These are the building blocks of atoms i.e. the fundamental particles of which all matter is made. At our level of science we concern ourselves with three of them, **electrons**, **neutrons** and **protons**. Of these the electron has no internal structure and so counts as a truly fundamental particle. Neutrons and protons do have an internal structure. Neutrons which are not in the nucleus are unstable and decay into a proton, an electron (and an antineutrino). Protons are believed to be made of particles known as quarks.

Element A substance consisting entirely of atoms of the same **atomic number**, i.e. each of the atoms in a sample of pure element will have the same number of electrons (their masses may be different though, see isotopes). Nitrogen (N, atomic number 7), iron (Fe, atomic number 26) and praseodymium (Pr, atomic number 59) are three examples of elements. There are 92 naturally occurring elements and about 15 synthetic ones. The synthetic ones are **radioactive** and very short lived, decaying to some other element within a few seconds (see the periodic table at the back for a list of elements).

Ellipse This is a plane figure. It is formed when a plane cuts obliquely through the axis of a right angled cone. We can draw an ellipse by placing drawing pins in the two focal points, looping string over their points and running a pencil with its point trapped in the string around them. In an ellipse, the line ACB always has the same length no matter where C is on the ellipse. Planets follow very slightly elliptical paths around the sun.

Embryo The early stages in the development of plant or animals. In humans the term embryo is used during the first two months of pregnancy, the term foetus is used once it can be recognised as human.

EMF See electromotive force.

Emmiter One of the three electrodes of a transistor.

Empirical Based on experiment and observation rather than on theory.

Empirical formula In chemistry this term means the simplest formula for a substance which gives only the proportions of the elements present rather than the actual numbers of atoms of each, so glucose has the empirical formula CH_2O but is actually $C_6H_{12}O_6$.

Emulsion A substance in which one liquid is dispersed as particles through another e.g. salad dressing is an emulsion in which tiny oil droplets are spread through egg yolk.

Enamel 1. The outer covering of the exposed part of teeth (two thirds calcium phosphate, one third calcium carbonate with about 3% composed of organic molecules e.g. proteins).
2. Vitreous enamel has glass–like properties being made from silica with other minerals added for colour or texture. It can be fused onto hot metal or pottery .

- 47 -

Endocrine gland A gland which does not give off its secretions into a duct but releases them into the blood stream (they are also known as the ductless glands). Oestrogen (ovaries and uterus), testosterone (testes), adrenaline (glands above the kidneys), growth hormone and menstrual cycle hormones (pituitary gland of the brain) and insulin (part of the pancreas) are all examples of hormones released by endocrine glands (the gland name is in brackets). These glands all have a good blood supply.

Endoplasmic reticulum (E R) A network of flattened spaces in the cytoplasm that are bounded by membranes. They provide routes for substances to move about inside the cell without coming into contact with the rest of the cytoplasm. They are often covered with granules (ribosomes) and are the places where proteins are synthesised.

ribosomes

rough E R

0.1μ

smooth E R

Endoskeleton A skeleton within the body as in vertebrates. Its bones are moved by muscles that act in pairs (antagonistic pairs).

Endosperm Plant seeds are made of an embryo plant, a supply of nutrient and a seed coat. The starchy nutrient is known as endosperm. Wheat endosperm is the main ingredient in bread.

Endothermic During an endothermic reaction there is a decrease in the temperature of the surroundings (see also exothermic).

Energy The term is not easy to define, after all, how do you define something that you can't touch, see or smell? Energy is usually defined as a capacity to do work. Its effects can be 'seen' in many ways e.g. heating up of brakes when cars slow down. It cannot be created or destroyed but can be transferred from one form to another (matter can be changed to energy). It is only possible to have complete transfer of energy to heat energy from the other forms. This is the only direction in which there can be 100% efficiency. For example it just isn't possible to convert all the energy in some fuel to electricity. A percentage of the energy will always appear as heat. **Symbol: E. Unit:** joule (J).

Energy transfer e.g. energy in the form of sunlight can be absorbed by plant leaves, used to split water and carbon dioxide and then saved in the form of sugars. There has been a transfer of energy from light to plant substances.

Engine All engines use some form of fuel, i.e. they transfer energy from substances to mechanical energy. All engines are machines but not all machines are engines. See-saws and bottle openers are machines but not engines. The arm or leg bones and the muscles that make them work are the engines (fuel is involved).

mmmm ! How long would I need to boil these to get them back straight again ?

Entropy In general terms, entropy can be thought of as the amount of disorder in the system. Entropy tends to increase. It is much easier to shuffle cards than to sort them out again. As an example; the energy in the sun is being spread through the galaxy every second. Each second, the sun gets smaller, matter changes to energy and energy spreads out through space. i.e. entropy is on the increase i.e. our universe is becoming more disordered. Symbol; S.

Environment An organism's environment is everything that surrounds it: climate, soils, geography, other organisms, water etc..

Enzyme Biological catalyst. Enzymes are protein molecules produced by living cells. Enzymes speed up reactions so that life is possible at the temperatures existing on earth. It is easy to get the impression that enzymes are only involved with the digestion. This is quite wrong. Every cell contains several thousand enzymes, a few of these will break down molecules, others will change molecules and others will build up molecules. Before substances can react, they need a certain amount of energy. Enzymes do their work by allowing the reaction to happen at lower energies. They have shapes that fit the chemicals in the reaction (substrates) and hold them in the right position long enough for the reaction to happen. They can do this very quickly and repeatedly (Catalase, which breaks down H_2O_2 to H_2O & O_2 , can catalyse 40 0000 molecule–splits each second) Enzymes are not broken down during the reactions and so they are only needed in very small amounts. They are slowly damaged in the same way that most complex molecules within cells are damaged so they won't last forever.

these molecules are free in solution, buffeting about all the time

active site on the enzyme

an instant later **B** and **A** have fitted into the active site and can now be joined together

Epicentre The point on the surface directly above the focus of the earthquake (see Earthquake for a diagram).

Epidermis A protective layer on the outside of multicellular organisms.

Epiglottis A flap in the oesophagus that helps prevent food entering the trachea.

Epithelium Tissue which lines cavities or tubes in the body e.g. the lining of the intestine, bladder, or nasal passages.

Equation 1. In chemistry we use symbols to represent the atoms involved in a reaction and set them out to show the amounts of reactants and products.

word equation —— metal carbonates + acids = salt + carbon dioxide + water

$$MgCO_{3(s)} + H_2SO_{4(aq)} = MgSO_{4(aq)} + CO_{2(g)} + H_2O_{(l)}$$

before the reaction   after the reaction

2. In maths an equation is a way of stating that the part on the left equals the part on the right e.g. $3 + 3 + 7 = 13$ or $5x + 6 = 26$.

Equilibrium 1. A state of balance e.g. the population of the U.K. is in equilibrium because the death rate + emigration equals the birth rate + immigration. This sort of balance is called dynamic equilibrium because a balance exists while even though change is going on.
2.Many chemical reactions take place in both directions so that eventually a state of dynamic equilibrium exists e.g. hydrogen ions and hydroxide ions combine to give water. The reaction can be written as:

$$H^+_{(aq)} + OH^-_{(aq)} \rightleftharpoons H_2O_{(l)}$$

Equinox Twice a year the sun crosses the equator and at that time, day and night are of equal length. This time is the equinox. (i.e. day and night as defined by sunrise and sunset times, dawn and dusk will make the day seem longer though).

Erg A tiny unit of work or energy no longer in use. 1 erg = 10^{-7} Joule.

Ergometer   A device for measuring energy transfer e.g. the hand wheel that you used when measuring the power of the arm, or the mounted bicycle for measuring the power of your legs.

Erosion   The wearing away of the land's surface by wind or water. Soil is a fragile material and needs to be held in place by plant cover. Ploughing, grazing animals, the feet of livestock and cutting down of forests all make soil more likely to be eroded. As most of our food production needs soil, we need to take soil erosion very seriously. Preventing erosion: 1.   Plough along the contours rather than up and down the slopes. 2.   Keep the crop foliage on the ground for as long as possible. 3. Leave windbreaks along the edges of the fields. 4.   Maintain the humus content of the soil as, in humus–rich soils, the sand particles are bound together by gummy material into little lumps which are less likely to be blown away. 5.   Use hardy plants like Marram grass to bind the loose soil together.

Erythrocyte   Red blood cell (see blood cell).

Escape velocity   Any object that must escape our Earth's gravity field has to be travelling at 25 000 miles per hour (11 200 ms^{-1}). Each planet or moon will have its own escape velocity and this will depend on its mass and diameter.

Essential amino acids   Amino acids (the building blocks of proteins) that an organism cannot manufacture for itself and which must therefore be present in its diet.

Essential element   Any element required by an organism e.g. iron for vertebrates.

Essential fatty acids   In the case of humans, linoleic acid and gamma–linoleic acids have to be present in the diet, or scaly skin, hair loss, poor growth and death will occur.

Ester   Many esters have a pleasant smell and are used as flavouring for food. These organic compounds are made when an organic group reacts with a carboxylic acid: Ethanol (drinking alcohol) and ethanoic acid (vinegar) will react to give the ester ethyl ethanoate. $C_2H_5OH + CH_3CO_2H = CH_3CO_2C_2H_5$

Ethane   A colourless odourless gas that forms an explosive mixture with air (C_2H_6).

Ethanoic acid   Vinegar is a 2 – 4% solution of ethanoic acid (CH_3CO_2H)

Ethanol   The alcohol found in drinks and used as a fuel. It is a colourless, flammable | this hydrogen is an essential part of the acid. It can separate from the molecule as a hydrogen ion. |
liquid with a very low freezing point (– 115°C) and a boiling point of 78·3°C .

Ethers   Organic compounds in which two carbon containing groups are joined together by an oxygen. They are made by reacting two alcohols together e.g. the well known anaesthetic, di-ethyl ether is made by reacting two ethanol molecules to get $C_2H_5-O-C_2H_5$

Eukaryotic   Organisms like our good selves, whose cells contain a nucleus, mitochondria and other organelles, are known as eukaryotes.   Most multicellular organisms are eukaryotic. Bacteria are known as prokaryotes, their cells do not contain a nucleus.

Eutrophic   Rich in nutrients. This can be a good thing, as where upwelling in the sea brings up nutrients, plant plankton flourishes and rich fishing grounds result. It can also be bad, where sewage or other organic matter is released into rivers or lakes and allows algae, fungi and bacteria to increase rapidly, depleting oxygen and killing the more acceptable inhabitants like fish.

Evaporation   Occurs when particles of matter leave the surface of liquid or solid. You know that brass and beeswax have their own smell. This is only possible if particles are leaving these substances and being breathed in across your nasal linings. i.e. the brass and beeswax are evaporating. Energy will be lost from the liquid or solid.

Even   Divisible by 2. Even numbers are all the whole numbers that are divisible by 2.

Evolution   Darwin / Wallace theory: There is always variation within a species (tall, short, fast, slow, fat, thin, able to withstand cold conditions better, more efficient user of food, etc).   Because offspring so often resemble their parents, we know that these variations can be passed on.

There are always more offspring produced than can possibly survive so that, on average, it will be the 'best suited' who have the best chance of surviving (for every 2 blackbirds that survive to breed in your garden, about 10 will have died without breeding). This steady removal of less than perfect organisms before they can breed will tend to stabilise the species keeping it suited to its environment. Provided the environment remains constant, species will not change for long periods. However, if the environment changes (gets wetter, warmer, etc) then new models of existing organisms may be more likely to survive and breed. Darwin and Wallace put forward a theory as to how all these changes could have occurred. Since then scientists have discovered many of the mechanisms (the transfer of genes from parent to offspring, mutations, jumping genes) that are involved during the process of evolution.

Excretion   The loss from the organism of metabolic waste products which might prove toxic if allowed to build up in the body. E.g. most animals are constantly producing carbon dioxide which has the effect of lowering the body's pH. It must therefore be removed. In vertebrates this is done through gills or lungs. The lungs, kidneys and liver are excretory organs in vertebrates. Many plants deposit metabolic wastes in leaves just before they are shed in autumn.   It is important to realise that excretion is not just the release of undigested food (as faeces), this is termed **egestion.**

Exoskeleton   A skeleton that covers the outside of the body as is found in insects, crustacea and other arthropods.

Exothermic   During an exothermic reaction heat is given out and the chemicals may feel warm; they may even glow or be part of a flame.

EE button (EXP) The button on your calculator that allows you to do calculations with powers of ten. Should you need to multiply 44·5 million by 7·3419 billion. This can be done by pressing 44·5 EE 6 x 7·3419 EE 7 = 3·2304 x 10^{15} .

Expansion   This is the process by which things get larger !
1.   When the particles in a mass of material vibrate or bounce harder they will move further apart. In other words the lump of material will expand.
2.   We can make the particles vibrate or bounce harder by heating the object. For most substances, raising the temperature causes expansion.

Further detail: There are forces inside the object that hold all the particles together. If these were the only forces in the object then the particles would collapse together and the object would be very small and very dense. This is not the case and so we conclude that a balance exists between the forces holding the mass of matter together and those forces causing it to expand.

Expanding Universe   If we look at any of the galaxies around our own galaxy they all seem to be moving away from us. Those galaxies that are furthest away seem to be moving away the fastest. It seems reasonable to assume that our universe is expanding. The rate at which the galaxies are moving away is calculated by measuring the amount of red shift due to the **doppler effect** in the light we see from them.

Explanation   Be on your guard when people offer explanations (this warning extends to the explanations in this guide), for explanations are often little more than a rewording of the question. There is a story that in the last century, some doctors set out to discover why opium causes drowsiness. Their explanation was that the opium contains the substance 'vis dormifera'

                      /   \

     substance   that sends you to sleep   (i.e. not an explanation at all !)

Exponential. If you were to draw a graph using the equation y = 3ˣ, you could very easily get the graph on the right.
Typically, such a graph gets steeper and steeper as x gets larger. We say that such a graph shows an 'exponential increase'.

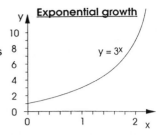

$$10^4 \overset{\text{power (or exponent)}}{\underset{\text{base}}{\Big\langle}}$$

Exponential growth and decay Explosive growth such as shown in the graph above. When no competition occurs between individuals in a population and there is no predation or disease, the population will increase exponentially. This sort of growth occurs in the early stages in bacteria or cell cultures.
An example of exponential decay is provided by the pattern of change of radiation given off by a set piece of radioactive material.

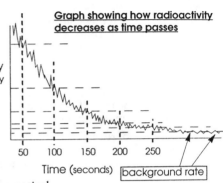

Extrapolation Using judgement (or some mathematical method) to extend ones results beyond what is known. If we have to hurry an experiment and so only get 3 results but need to know what the length of the spring would be when the force is 3 newtons. The dotted extension is our extrapolation (see also interpolation).

Eye See accommodation.

Eyepiece The lens of an optical system that is nearest the eye.

Fact A fact is something that is known to be true or something that has happened. History shows that we need to be very careful of facts. Mistakes are easily made so that some of the 'facts' like 'The earth is flat', 'Witches can cause the crops to fail', 'The earth is at the centre of the solar system', once believed to be true, are now known to be seriously suspect.

Factors These are best explained by giving an example. In the case of 4 x 6 = 24, the 4 and 6 are factors of 24. 24 is divisible by 4 and 6. 1, 2, 3, and 12 are also factors of 24.

Fahrenheit scale A temperature scale in which the melting point of ice was set at 32° and the boiling point of water at 212°. $1\,^{\circ}C = \dfrac{212 - 32}{100}\,^{\circ}F$ i.e. $1\,^{\circ}C = \dfrac{9}{5}\,^{\circ}F$

Fall-out Radioactive particles that settle from the atmosphere. In the past fall-out came mainly from atmospheric nuclear explosions. More recently there has been fall-out from mishaps at nuclear reactors, in particular from Chernobyl in the Ukraine.

Fallopian tube The tube down which eggs pass from ovary to uterus in female mammals. Fertilisation takes place in the fallopian tubes.

- 52 -

Fat (and oil) Chemicals made mostly of carbon and hydrogen atoms with some oxygen. They have a number of properties that allow us to put them in the same group.
1. they float (are less dense than water)
2. they burn well, releasing lots of energy for a given weight of fat
3. they are insoluble in water (our blood has special chemicals just for carrying them about)
4. they are made by joining fatty acids to glycerol.

This is the carboxylic acid part (like the acid part of vinegar or citric acid)

Fatty acid Most of the fatty acid molecule is made of carbon and hydrogen. They burn, giving off energy. Over 70 different fatty acids have been isolated from nature, most of these contain 15 to 18 carbon atoms. In the diagram, the dots (....) represent more carbon atoms. If these middle carbon atoms have less that 2 hydrogen each, they are said to be 'unsaturated', i.e. not saturated with hydrogen.

Fatty acid molecule

Fatty part / Acid part

Fatty acids and glycerol The fats that we all know about, lard, dripping etc., are composed of large molecules in which 3 fatty acids are joined to glycerol to form a triglyceride.

Triglyceride

Faults Points of rupture or fracture of rock strata due to the forces that act on them (strain). Faults can be small, <10 m. or huge, the fault that formed the Great Glen in Scotland caused the land on either side of the fault to move about 100 km.

Fecundity The ability to produce offspring. For example lemmings and other rodents have a very high fecundity.

the fatty acids join on to the carbon atoms here

Feedback Any process in which the output controls the input in some way.
Negative feedback is much more common because it has so many applications. The flow of water into the loo cistern, the regulation of body temperature in mammals and birds and the rate of many chemical reactions in living cells are all controlled by negative feedback mechanisms. **Positive feedback** As an example consider the birth of a baby. This begins when the **uterus** contracts. These contractions stretch the **cervix** (the opening of the uterus). Stretching the cervix causes the release of a substance which makes the contractions stronger, therefore the cervix is more stretched, therefore more of the substance is released and so on until the baby is born (or until the mother's and baby's life are in danger).

Fehling's test This is a test for certain sugars (reducing sugars like fructose, glucose). The solution contains copper sulphate ($CuSO_4$), sodium hydroxide (NaOH) and potassium sodium tartrate.
The test: Add 2 cm^3 of the solution of reducing sugar to a test tube. Add 1 cm^3 of Fehling's solution A and 1 cm^3 of Fehling's solution B. Shake and bring to the boil. If a reducing sugar is present the solution first turns green, then yellow and finally a brick red precipitate forms. (see also Benedict's, and the tests for protein; Biuret's and Millon's).

Fermentation Commonly, we think of fermentation as a way of producing alcohol by using yeasts to break down the sugars in grape juice or malted barley. Correctly though, the term is used for any anaerobic respiration e.g. as it occurs in hard-working muscles when they produce lactic acid.

Fermi A unit of length which is useful in nuclear physics. 1 Fermi = 10^{-15}m

Ferrite materials   These all contain iron oxide (Fe_2O_3) together with another oxide e.g. cobalt, nickel. zinc or manganese. The material can be moulded into rods and used to make magnets of any shape and also used to make ferrite rods to be used as aerials for radios (ferrite rods are not used for F.M. frequencies).

Ferritin   A protein that contains iron as Fe^{2+}. Iron stores in the mammalian liver, spleen and bone marrow are in the form of ferritin.

Ferromagnetic materials   These materials can be magnetised by using weak magnetic fields. The chief ferromagnetic materials are **iron, cobalt** and **nickel**. These three metals will retain their magnetism at normal temperatures.
Before they are magnetised all the atoms within a piece of ferromagnetic material behave as little magnets with their magnetic fields arranged in every direction. When the piece becomes magnetised all the clusters of atoms (**domains**) have their **magnetic fields** arranged in the same direction so that the fields add together to give a measurable effect. (see also Curie temperature).

Fertilisation   The whole point of this process is to mix together genes from the two parents (half from each parent). This mixing will produce offspring that are not exact copies of the parents, i.e. each new generation will contain many different varieties and these can be acted upon by natural selection.   Most aquatic creatures have external fertilisation, the sperm and eggs are released into the water and fertilisation occurs outside the body.   Most terrestrial animals have internal fertilisation. In plants, the pollen (which will produce the male **gamete**) is transferred from the male flower, or male parts of the flower, to the stigma by insects, water or wind (see also gamete and zygote).

Fertiliser   These are compounds of elements that are essential for healthy plant life. Most fertilisers contain nitrogen compounds, phosphorus compounds and potassium salts. Organic fertilisers like manure or compost also contain these three.

Fibre optics   The subject that studies the ability of fine glass fibres to convey light over long distances with little loss in intensity. Because the fibres are very fine they can be bent without breaking and will carry the light around corners. Bundles of these fibres with lens systems at either end can be used to view otherwise inaccessible places, the human gut, the inside of working machinery. Optical fibres are becoming increasingly important as a way of carrying telephone messages and other forms of communication. The fibres work because, once inside, light is kept inside by total internal reflection (see critical angle).

Fibrin   A protein found in the blood that is involved in the formation of blood clots. Under the right conditions it forms a mesh of fibres which stick to the sides of the wound and draw them together as the wound dries out.

Field   This is a region where a force is felt e.g. the electric field around a Van de Graaff generator dome, the magnetic field around a bar magnet, the gravitational field around a lump of matter.

Field lines   are used to help us get a picture of the electric, magnetic or gravitational field. The convention is that the lines are close together in those regions where the field is strongest.

Film badge   A strip of film, covered to protect it from light, which is worn by people whose work involves exposure to radioactivity. Every few days a new film strip is supplied and the old film is then developed. The amount of darkening gives a measure of the radiation dosage received by the worker.

Filter feeders   These creatures get their food by sifting it from the water around them. Many crustacea (e.g. water fleas) have legs covered in bristles which they beat in the water to collect food. Muscles and other bivalves are also filter feeders.

Filtrate The clear liquid that has passed through the filtering material.

Filtration A way of separating a liquid from solid particles suspended in it.

Fission bomb Fission means splitting. A fission bomb usually contains uranium, plutonium or thorium. Atoms of these can be triggered to split into fragments releasing huge amounts of energy and radiation. Radio-isotopes will be formed e.g. Caesium.

Fixation (usually; fixation of nitrogen) Certain bacteria are able to change nitrogen gas into nitrates, the most well-known of these occur in the root nodules of plants of the bean family (Legumes). The Haber process provides an industrial way of doing the same thing and is very important in the manufacture of fertilisers and explosives.

Fixed stars All the stars, none of the planets. The stars keep their positions compared with one another but the position of planets against the stars, keeps changing.

Flagellum A long thread, which projects from some living cells and , which is able to beat , causing the cell to move along (or fluid to flow past the cell). Flagella usually occur singly and are much longer than cilia. Cilia usually cover the whole of a surface of a cell as happens on the cells lining our trachea. The Paramecium on page 5 is covered with cilia, the Chlamydomonas on page 7 has two flagellae.

Flame A region containing glowing gas that has been produced during **combustion**. A candle flame contains hot gas and wax vapour that are still reacting with oxygen.

Flash point This is the lowest temperature at which a substance gives off enough flammable vapour to cause a momentary flame if a spark were to be applied. The flash point is not the point at which spontaneous combustion occurs.

Flemings left hand rule The rule that tells us which way a conductor in a magnetic field will move when a current flows through it.

Thumb →	motion
First →	magnetic field
SeCond →	Current

Flip flop An electronic switch that is stable in 2 positions.

Flower Reproductive shoot of a flowering plant. The diagram below shows the main parts of an insect-pollinated flower. Wind pollinated flowers, e.g. wheat or barley, are usually much simpler.

Fluid A substance with the properties of a liquid i.e. a fluid flows to take the shape of its container. Moving fluids show certain properties (see Bernoulli) and many substances that we don't normally think of as fluids e.g. the snow in an avalanche can show fluid properties.

Fluorescence Fluorescent substances will glow when they are struck by light or by electrons. The light given out usually has a longer wavelength (i.e. it is towards the redder end of the spectrum) than the light that caused the fluorescence. T. V. screens have their inside face coated with fluorescent chemicals. **Zinc sulphide, beryllium** and other metal compounds will give off fluorescence. If the luminescence (i.e. the glow) fades as soon as the source of energy is removed, we call it fluorescence, if it persists, we call it phosphorescence.

Fluorescent tubes A glass tube which contains mercury vapour and so gives off ultra violet light when a current flows through the vapour. The fluorescent powder on the inside of the tube glows brightly when struck by ultraviolet rays.

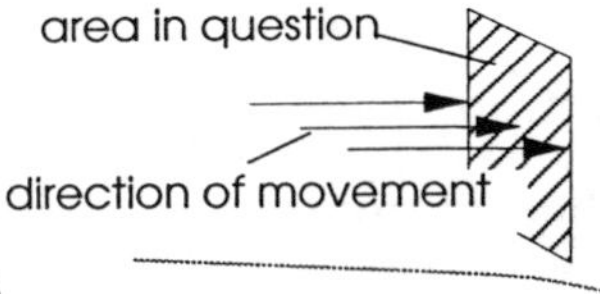

Flux   Flux is the rate of flow of something through an area which is at right angles to the flow.

area in question

direction of movement

Fold   These occur because the rocks of the earth's crust are compressed with enough sideways force to cause flexing or bending.

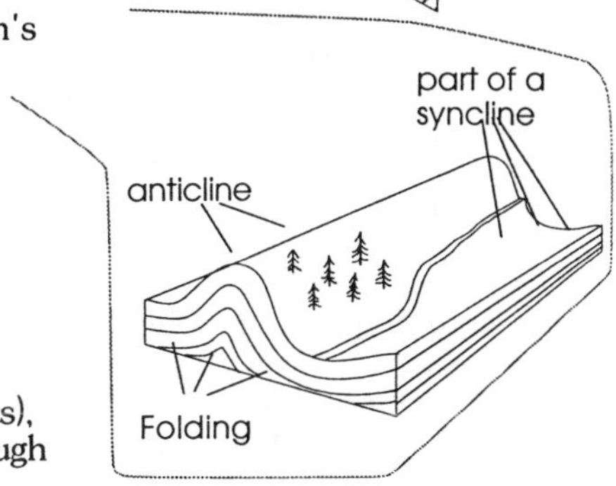

part of a syncline

Follicle stimulating hormone   A substance produced by a part of the vertebrate brain. It controls the production of eggs in the ovaries and stimulates the production of sperm in the testes. It is a small protein.

anticline

Folding

Food   Most animals need a daily supply of energy–providing foods (carbohydrates and fats), foods for growth and repair (proteins) and enough water, mineral salts, vitamins and roughage.
Plants do not need substances that provide energy and so it is wrong to talk about food for plants in science. Plants get their energy from sunlight and get mineral salts from the soil.

Food chain   Here is an example :   grass ──► termites ──► aardvark ──► leopard

A moment of reflection will show that food chains don't really represent the world of nature. Each of the organisms in the chain shown above, are food for several different organisms, i.e. they are part of a web and we only set them out as links in a chain for simplicity.

Food web.   A food web shows **all** the interactions (who consumes what or whom) within a community of organisms.

Foot   (length) A unit of length in the imperial system, 1 foot = 0·3048 m .
(biology) A stunningly well–designed lever system made of bones linked with ligaments that allow bipedals like ourselves to more than double our top speed. If you doubt this, try running on your heels without using the balls of your feet.

Force   A force is a push or a pull. Simple as that! (see centripetal force).
Units: 1 newton is the force that will accelerate 1 kg by 1 ms^{-2} ($1N = 1 kg . ms^{-2}$)
Symbol: F

Formula.   Formulae are used in Science and Maths to show a rule. We use symbols or figures for this. e.g. $F = m a$, $S = ut + \frac{1}{2} at^2$, K.E. = $\frac{1}{2} mv^2$ etc.
In chemistry formulae give us a shorthand way of writing a compound or molecule e.g. magnesium chloride can be written $Mg Cl_2$. Formulae for some common substances are given at the back of the dictionary.

Fossil   This is the remains of an organism, or direct evidence of its presence, preserved in rock, ice, amber, tar, peat or volcanic ash. Only the more recent fossils contain the chemicals that were part of the organism. In older fossils, the original material has been leached away and replaced by minerals, often calcite or silica.

Fossil fuel   Peat, coal, oil or natural gas are all fossil fuels. They are called fossil fuels because they are composed of the organic remains of organisms that have become entombed in rock.

Fourth dimension   A system which uses our three dimensions of space, with time, the added dimension.

Fractional distillation   This process allows us to separate a mixture into a number of parts depending on the boiling points of the different parts. As an example, we use fractional distillation to separate crude oil into tar, grease, heavy oils, paraffin, petrol etc.

Free electron These electrons are not permanently attached to any particular atom and so they will move if an electric field is placed across their space. Most metals have free electrons which can be made to move i.e. form a current. (The term is also used to refer to unpaired electrons in atoms also known as odd electrons)

Free fall That state in which an object is falling under the influence of gravity. In a vacuum the object continues to accelerate until it collides. Objects falling in the atmosphere will speed up until drag equals accelerating force. They then continue falling at constant speed.

Free radicals Molecules or ions that have an unpaired electron (this makes most of them very reactive). Some, like atmospheric oxygen (O_2) and NO_2 are not very reactive (see radical).

Freeze drying A technique for removing water from something without having to make it so hot that chemical changes occur. It is very useful in the preparation of coffee powder, dried soups and other convenience foods.

Freon This is the trade name for a group of substances, the chlorofluorocarbons. They have been widely used as the coolant in transformers and in the cooling mechanism in fridges. They have been shown to be very damaging to the ozone layer.

Frequency The number of waves that pass a point every second. More accurately it is the number of complete oscillations or cycles in a unit of time.
Symbol : v or f. Unit: hertz (Hz) 1 hertz = 1 cycle per second.
Formula: frequency $= \dfrac{\text{velocity}}{\text{wavelength}}$

Friable Something that is easily crumbled. Most shales are friable whereas granite is not.

Friction The slowing down force noticed when one body slides over another. Sliding friction: the force needed to keep one body just sliding over another is known as **dynamic** friction. The force that is needed to start two objects sliding over each other is slightly larger and is known as the **static** or **limiting** friction. Rolling friction is the force resisting the rolling of a body on a plane surface. Friction increases approximately in proportion to the force that presses the two surfaces together and does not depend on area.

Frontal lobes The part of the brain just behind the forehead. They are part of the cerebral cortex and seem to play a part in personality.

Fuel This is a material that can release energy on burning, e.g. fuel oils, coal, natural gas, synthetic gases, and rocket fuels. Strictly, uranium and plutonium are not fuels as they release energy without needing to be burnt.

Fuel element Fuel elements contain the nuclear fuel used in nuclear reactors. The elements usually contain uranium oxide.

Full wave rectification The diagram on the right shows how we can arrange 4 diodes so that they change alternating current (a.c.) into direct current (d.c.). As the voltage and current are constantly changing in most a.c. supplies, the voltage of the d.c. output will also be changing. We can produce a nearly stable d.c. current by adding a capacitor as shown in this diagram.

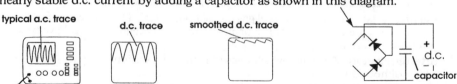

Fungi Fungi contain no chlorophyll and can be single celled (e.g. yeasts) or multicellular (e.g. mushrooms). Many play a very important part in the decay that goes on all around us.

Fungicide Fungicides slow down or stop fungal attack, e.g. on roots and leaves of crop plants, on seeds at sowing time, on fruit or grain, on the pulp collecting behind the rollers in paper mills or sugar beet factories. Important fungicides include sulphur, polysulphides and other sulphur–containing substances, heavy metals (Copper, Tin, Mercury and Nickel). Some sources claim that there is no evidence that fungicides have caused any major environmental problems but it is known that the fungicide seed dressing can accumulate in pigeons and partridges and then in the birds of prey that eat them.

Fur (in kettles) Mainly calcium carbonate, magnesium carbonate and/or iron carbonate. These are insoluble and so settle on the inside of the kettle as they form. They are produced from soluble hydrogen carbonates when the water is heated.

Fuse Fuses are used to protect circuits from overheating and for safeguarding people from nasty shocks. They melt when too much current flows in a circuit. Circuits that carry large currents, like those in houses, can produce enough heat to cause fires and so household fuses play a very important part of keeping houses safe. The alloys used in fuses must have low resistance so that they don't reduce the current very much but they must also have a low melting point.

A diagram showing the position of a fuse placed to protect both the kettle and the person using it.

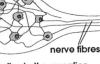

Fusion bomb (or reactor) Fusion, in this sense, means joining together of atoms to form a larger atom. e.g. two hydrogen atoms join together to form helium. The helium produced has smaller mass than the hydrogen that produced it. This missing mass has appeared as energy, very large amounts of energy and so the process can be used mischievously in bombs (the hydrogen bomb) or as an energy source in a fusion reactor (not yet practical). The process requires temperatures greater than 40 million degrees C and at these temperatures the walls of the container keep melting. In the hydrogen bomb, a fission bomb is used to raise the temperature enough to get the reaction started (see hydrogen bomb).

Galaxy A collection of gas, stars and dust (plus dark matter). Most galaxies occur in groups which move together. Each galaxy can contain a few million million stars.

Gallon A British Imperial gallon is equal to 4·54609 cubic decimetres (4·54609 litres). 0·83268 British gallons = 1 U.S. gallon

Galvanise To cover iron with a layer of zinc, usually by dipping in molten zinc. It is done to reduce corrosion. A little magnesium or aluminium is added to prevent a brittle alloy of iron and zinc from forming.

Gamete These are cells (sometimes just a nucleus, as in the pollen tube) that are specialised for fertilisation. Because male and female gametes fuse, each gamete has only half the genetic material needed by the offspring . Cells which have only half of the genetic material are called haploid cells (see diploid) .

Gametocyte A cell which will produce gametes (after meiosis).

Gamma rays Given off by certain radioactive substances. They are rays of electromagnetic radiation of very short wavelength which can penetrate several metres of concrete. They are not deflected by magnetic or electric fields. Wavelengths range from 3·9 x 10^{-10} m to 4·7 x 10^{-13} m. Gamma rays are given off due to energy changes within the nuclei of atoms. They are very dangerous rays.

Ganglion Groups of nerve tissue in which there are many cell bodies so that the region is thicker than other parts of the nerve. In the ganglion many nerve fibres end on each cell body. Because of these connections, nerve signals are co-ordinated and controlled. Ganglia are a feature of invertebrate nervous systems.
(Medical) A ganglion is a swelling along part of a tendon.

the ganglion

nerve fibres

linked cell bodies in the ganglion

Gas Gases fill the space in which they are placed i.e. the overall forces between the particles are not large enough to hold them together (as would happen in liquid or solid).

Gas chromatography A sensitive way of identifying the components in a mixture of organic substances. The method works with very tiny samples and so it is useful in biochemistry where we often can only get small samples. It is particularly suited to separating volatile substances.

Gas cooled reactor (e.g. Magnox reactor) High pressure gas is used to transfer energy from the reactor core to the steam generator.

Gas laws Statements about how the volume of a gas changes as we alter the temperature and pressure (see Boyle's law and Charles' law).

Gastric Of the stomach. As in gastric ulcer, a region of damaged tissue in the stomach wall.

Gastropod A class of organisms in the group Mollusca i.e. snails, slugs, limpets etc.

Gene This is a short length of chromosome that carries the information needed to produce a single length of protein (a polypeptide chain). We normally think of genes as controlling the appearance of organisms. Chromosomes contain both DNA and protein. It is the DNA that carries the genetic code.

Gene pool All the genes in a genetic population (an interbreeding population). Any individual cannot have all of these genes e.g. although there are genes for every hair colour in the U.K. population, each person will only have a few of these.

Genetic code Each gene has the code needed to make a particular length of protein. Proteins are made from about 20 different amino acids and the purpose of the gene is to ensure that these amino acids are joined together in the correct order. The code for any one amino acid is a short length of DNA or RNA which has 3 bases (see codon and protein synthesis).

Genetic drift In small populations there is always a chance that some of the genes will not be passed on to the the next generation. Genetic drift is the change in the gene pool due to genes being lost from the population because of its small size. This loss is unlikely to occur in large populations.

Genetic fingerprinting A way of staining and displaying DNA taken from samples of tissue. The method is able to highlight very small differences between individuals and so is being used in court cases as a way of linking suspects to hair or other tissue left at the scene of a crime. It has many other uses e.g. tracking population migrations.

Genitalia External reproductive organs (very important in insect identification).

Genito–urinary diseases Diseases that affect the reproductive or urinary system. Many cases are not due to sexual transmission (65% in 1992/93). If you feel you may have contracted such a disease it is important to have it treated quickly. Because many people are embarrassed about these ailments the rules allow you to visit a doctor other than your normal doctor and you can also refer yourself directly to the Genito–urinary medicine department (G U M) of your local hospital.

Genome The total genetic material of an organism or cell.

Genotype The genetic make–up of an individual. (see also phenotype).

Genus A group of organisms with many similar characteristics. Genus fits between family and species in the classification system. Our genus is Homo, the genus for the dog group is Canis and Oaks belong to the genus Quercus. (see classification)

Geological period See the table below.

Period	Time (millions of years ago)	Organisms found	Era
Quaternary		Humans	Cenozoic
Tertiary		Mammals, birds and insects, flowering plants	Cenozoic
Cretaceous	100	First placental mammals, extinction of dinosaurs Gymnosperms decreasing, Increasingly diverse flowering plants	Mesozoic
Jurassic		Dinosaurs abundant, first birds and egg-laying mammals Gymnosperms are common, first angiosperms	Mesozoic
Triassic	200	First dinosaurs, reptiles dominant, first mammals	Mesozoic
Permian		Early reptiles	Paleozoic
Carboniferous		Wide variety of amphibians, first reptiles and insects, giant horsetails and tree ferns	Paleozoic
Devonian	300	Many types of jawed fish, first amphibians, First giant horsetails and tree ferns	Paleozoic
Silurian	400	Jawed fish, Mosses well established	Paleozoic
Ordovician		Jawless fish, First mosses	Paleozoic
Cambrian	500 600	Sponges and molluscs, Many forms of algae	Paleozoic
Precambrian	700 3 000	Jellyfish and annelid worms, Bacteria and blue-green algae	Archaeozoic

Geometrical growth During this type of growth, each increase is a fixed proportion of the previous size (after equal intervals of time). For example, if a bacterial colony double each day the daily size tally could be something like : 20, 40, 80, 160, 320, 640, 1280 and so on. (numbers set out like this are part of a **geometric progression**). In the early stages of plants ' and animals ' lives, growth is geometrical or nearly so. It continues in this way until **limiting factors** begin to operate (see also exponential).

Graph showing how the height of a bean plant changes with time

Height (cm.)

time (days)

Gestation The time between conception and birth for those animals that bear live offspring.

Giant structure Many atoms and ions are able to join together endlessly to form very large structures. The size of the final object depends on how much material is available. e.g. there is no limit to the size of a crystal of copper sulphate, other than the limit set by how much of the salt we have and the size of the container in which we are growing the crystal. Crystals like this are called **ionic giant structures** because they are composed of ions. Diamond, graphite, crystals of metals etc. are made of atoms, joined together in a regular way and we call these **atomic giant structures**.

Giberillins A group of plant growth substances that are involved in elongation of stems and seed germination.

Giga A prefix for one thousand million times (10^9). Symbol G e.g. GW : gigawatt

Gill 1. (Measure) A unit of volume. 1 gill = quarter of a pint = 0·142075 litres
   2. (Biology) A gas exchange surface for aquatic animals in many ways equivalent to lungs. Gills have a large surface area and a good blood supply.

Gizzard A muscular section in the alimentary tract of many birds, reptiles and crustacea that is useful for breaking up hard foods. The inside is lined with a very tough surface.

Glass A brittle mixture produced by melting silica with other substances. E.g. soft laboratory glass (soda glass) is mainly silica, mixed with sodium carbonate and lime. Special glass is produced for cooking utensils or for lenses. Glass forms a non–crystalline solid with particles arranged in a disordered way.

Globular cluster Clusters of about a hundred thousand stars. We can see hundreds of them in our Milky way i.e. in our own galaxy.

Glucagon A polypeptide hormone that is released from the pancreas when blood sugar levels fall. It brings about the release of glucose from most tissue but particularly from the liver.

Glucose ($C_6H_{12}O_6$) The most common 6 carbon sugar. It is the first sugar to appear during photosynthesis. It is an important blood sugar. Being water soluble it can get to most tissues quite quickly and is a useful rapidly mobilised source of energy. It is also a building block for glycogen, cellulose, chitin and other polymers.

Gluten A mixture of proteins found in wheat and rye flour. They are important in bread making as they form a very smooth sticky mass during kneading and this traps the bubbles of CO_2 released by the yeast cells.

Glycogen A substance found in liver and other cells that is made by linking many glucose molecules together. The large molecules (polymers) are not soluble in water and so remain where they are formed. The glucose can be released at any time.

Goblet cell Mucus producing cells found in the epithelium lining the respiratory tract and some other parts of the body.

Golgi apparatus A part of the cytoplasm (of cells) that has, as one of its functions, the secretion of substances from the cell. In electron micrographs golgi apparatus shows up as stacks of elongated spaces surrounded by membranes.

A section through Golgi apparatus

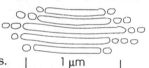

1 µm

Gonads The organs that produce eggs or sperm in animals.

Gondwanaland Two supercontinents that existed during the Mesozoic. The southern one, Gondwanaland, was composed of what we now call South America, Africa, India, Australia, Antarctica and New Zealand. Gondwanaland split from Laurasia about 130 million years ago (Myr B.P. i.e millions of years before present) (see continental drift, Laurasia).

Graafian follicles These are found in mammalian ovaries. They are fluid filled cavities that each contains an unfertilised egg. After the egg is released they change in form and start secreting oestrogens.

Gradient Slope. Usually this is used in connection with graphs. The gradients of graphs tell us at a glance (speed of information transfer is part of the beauty of graphs) how fast things are changing (i.e.rates of change). In the graph on the right the slope tells us what the speed was. The slope of the graph on the left shows us how busy the ticket sellers were at different times of the day.

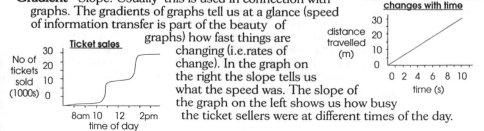

Ticket sales

No of tickets sold (1000s)

8am 10 12 2pm
time of day

Graph showing how distance changes with time

distance travelled (m)

0 2 4 6 8 10
time (s)

Gravity Sir **Isaac Newton** came to the conclusion that an attractive force exists between any two objects. The force will be greatest between large, dense masses which are close together. That is: 1. the larger the masses, the larger the force. 2. the closer the objects, the larger the force. This gravitational force is responsible for the circular motion of the planets. *Newton's law of universal gravitation states that any two particles of matter attract one another with a force which is proportional to the product of their masses and inversely proportional to the square of their distances apart.* (You get a product by multiplying two numbers together). (see proportionality constant)

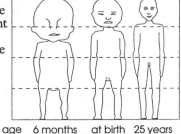

$$F \; \alpha \; \frac{mass_1 \; mass_2}{distance \; 2}$$

mass of the two object e.g. two objects

distance separating the two

$$F = \frac{G \; m_1 \; m_2}{x \; 2}$$

proportionality constant

Gray A measure of radiation. If you receive a dose of 1 Gray then a joule of energy has been transferred to each kg of your body.

Greenhouse effect The levels of carbon dioxide, methane and nitrogen oxides (NO_x) are rising in the atmosphere. These gases are believed to be reducing the amount of energy that leaves the Earth for outer space and so causing a steady but slow rise in the Earth's temperature.

Group A collection of elements with very similar properties e.g. lithium, sodium, potassium, rubidium, caesium, francium. On the periodic table each vertical column is a group.

Growth The process of increase. This could refer to money in the bank, size of crystals, cells or organisms. In the case of organisms, there are two ways in which they can grow: 1. Growth in which all the proportions do not change, as happens in fish and many invertebrates.
2. Growth in which the proportions change as the organism gets larger. The diagram on the right gives idea of how this happens in humans. In most multicellular animals it would seem that the cells are programmed to divide a certain number of times after which further growth is only possible because the existing cells get larger. Most cells are able to start dividing again should it be necessary to repair damage. (see exponential growth, geometrical growth, differentiation)

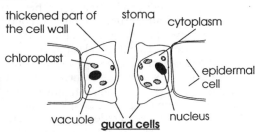

age   6 months   at birth   25 years

Guano A substance composed largely of bird excrement as well as the bodies of dead birds. It is found on islands with a very poor rainfall e.g. off the coast of Peru. Being very rich in nitrogen and phosphate compounds it is used as fertiliser.

Guard cells Specialised cells that surround the stoma in leaves and control the flow of gases (water, carbon dioxide and oxygen) into and out from the leaf. Guard cells differ from other leaf epidermal cells in that they have chloroplasts (their chloroplasts are not as well developed as chloroplasts in mesophyll cells) (see leaf for diagram).

thickened part of the cell wall

stoma

cytoplasm

chloroplast

epidermal cell

vacuole   **guard cells**   nucleus

Gymnophyta The group of plants that includes Conifers and Cycads. The seeds are not enclosed in an ovary wall.

Gyrocompass A compass that is based on a spinning wheel. It uses the principle that spinning wheels tend to hold their position in space (gyroscopic inertia).

Haber process This is used for preparing ammonia mainly for use in fertilisers. This is achieved by mixing hot nitrogen and hydrogen over a catalyst (iron) at 250 atmospheres pressure. $N_2 + 3H_2 \rightleftharpoons 2NH_3$

Habitat The natural home of an animal or plant. The term refers to everything that makes up this natural home, e.g. the soil, drainage, climate, and all the organisms present.

Haemoglobin A complex protein that is able to combine with oxygen in a reversible way i.e. it collects oxygen in the lungs or gills and releases it in the working tissues.

Half-life This is the time taken for something to reduce by half. My memory has a half-life of about 3 hours, i.e. after every 3 hours I have forgotten half of what I knew 3 hours ago. The term can be applied to lots of situations, e.g. the rate at which aspirin is lost from your body after you take some tablets or the rate at which a **radioactive** material **decays**. The half-lives of different radioactive materials can vary from millionths of a second to millions of years.

Element	Half-life
^{9}Lithium	0.17 sec.
^{38}Potassium	7.7 min.
^{55}Iron	2.7 yrs.
^{14}Carbon	5 570 yrs.
^{235}Uranium	4 500 000 yrs.

Halide Compounds formed when the elements in Group VII react e.g. fluoride, chloride, bromide, iodide. Many are ionic e.g. sodium chloride.

Halitosis See bad breath.

Halogen The elements in Group VII, namely; fluorine, chlorine, bromine, iodine and astatine.

Halophyte Plants that can tolerate very salty conditions like the conditions found on salt marshes along the North Norfolk coast.

Haploid Cells in which the chromosomes are single and unpaired. The letter n is used to represent the haploid condition (2n for diploid). (see meiosis).

Hard water Water that does not form a soapy lather easily. The reason for this is that the water contains compounds of calcium, magnesium (and iron). These substances react with the soap forming a scum.
There are two groups of substance causing hardness:
1. Hydrogen carbonates of the three metals. These are removed by boiling.
2. Sulphates of the three metals. These are not precipitated by boiling but can be made to react with washing soda crystals (Na_2CO_3 $10H_2O$)   (see fur).

Heart A pump that moves blood about. Hearts are found in all but the simplest creatures. In most arthropods the blood moves sluggishly and so the heart is just a simple muscular tube. In larger, more active organisms the blood is used to move oxygen and carbon dioxide about rapidly and so the heart in these creatures is more complex with 3 or 4 chambers.

Heat Energy that can be transferred between two bodies when there is a temperature difference. (Temperature is a reflection of the vibration of particles)

Heat capacity The quantity of energy needed to raise the temperature of a substance by 1° C (see specific thermal capacity).

Heat of formation The energy given out or absorbed when 1 mole of a compound is formed from its elements in their normal state.

Heat pump A device which can move energy from one space to another. The fridge cooling system is a good example. It can shift energy from inside the fridge to the air in the room. If it were redesigned so that the icy pipes inside the fridge were placed in a river flowing past the house it could be made to pump energy from the river to the house and so cut down heating costs.

Heavy metal The term is often used to refer to the metal elements with high atomic numbers which can be very toxic e.g. mercury, cadmium, lead, antimony and many others. Ions of many of these metals react readily with enzymes, damaging them and this is often how they produce their toxic effect.

Heavy water Water (H_2O) in which one or more hydrogens is replaced by a form of hydrogen known as deuterium.

Hydrogen nucleus: 1 proton.

Deuterium nucleus: 1 proton and 1 neutron i.e. hydrogen but twice the mass.

Tritium nucleus: 1 proton and 2 neutrons i.e. H with three times the mass.

Heavy water is used as a moderator in nuclear reactors i.e. a substance that slows down neutrons. HDO occurs in natural water: 1 part per 6000 of water. D_2O is much less common i.e. parts per million (see also deuterium, tritium, moderator).

Hectare 10 000 square metres i.e. 2·47105 acres.

Hemiptera A large group of insects that contain aphids, cicadas, bed bugs, shield bugs, leaf hoppers and scale insects.

Heparin A naturally produced substance that prevents blood from coagulating.

Herbicide Weedkiller. These can be grouped into **systemic** (those that are absorbed by the plant and so kill the roots as well as parts above the ground) and **contact** herbicides. It is now possible to have weedkillers that are selective in their action i.e. certain weedkillers can be sprayed on grain fields. They leave the crop plant unaffected but kill the broad–leafed weeds. Many herbicides affect chemical reactions that are not found in animals and so are harmless. Paraquat is **not** one of these, it is highly toxic to humans.

Herbivore Animals that feed largely, or entirely, on plants or plant products. Water fleas, weevils, carp, tortoises, dugongs (sea cows) and springbuck are all herbivores.

Heroin Diamorphine ($C_{21}H_{23}NO_5$). It can be produced from opium, is a powerful pain killer but not without side effects. It is fiercely addictive (see morphine).

Hertzsprung–Russell diagram A graph which has played an important part in our understanding of star evolution. In simple terms the graph plots brightness of stars against their colour.

Hertz The SI unit of frequency. 1 hertz = 1 cycle per second. It is a derived unit. Symbol: Hz Frequencies are often high so we have kilohertz and megahertz (1 megahertz = 1 million cycles per second).

Heterosome Sex chromosome.

Hibernation A condition that occurs in some warm blooded animals (homeotherms). There are marked changes in the animals physiology: the body temperature may drop to just 1° C above the surrounding temperature (ambient temp.). The basal metabolic rate drops to 1% of its normal value. It is common in mammals, particularly rodents. Many pet hamsters have been wrongly presumed to be dead.

Hierarchy An arrangement of people or things in a graded order. Algebraic hierarchy requires us to deal with an expression in a certain order.

Histogram A histogram is like a block graph in which the **areas** of each block represent the frequency. Area is important here. Often the class intervals are of equal width and so the heights of each block give a measure of the frequency. (This may seem to be a complicated definition but histograms are not the same as block graphs though the differences can be difficult to define)

Histology The study of the fine structure of tissues and organs.

HIV A group of viruses that can infect humans and which, over a period of time, bring about severe damage to their immune systems. They become unable to throw off infections that normally would not be life–threatening e.g. thrush. The person eventually dies from infections like pneumonia, encephalitis and hepatitis. The virus is usually transmitted through sexual contact.

Hole In electronics a hole can be created when an electron moves out of its position. The electrons which form part of a current will be drifting in one direction by leaving their position, moving on a bit and dropping into a hole. We can think of the current as being negative electrons drifting one way or positive holes moving in the other direction.

Homeostasis see negative feedback.

Hominid A group of organisms that move about on two legs (i.e they are bipedal). The shape of their bite and size of their brain (800 to 1600 cm³) are also features that separate them from other primates. Humans and human–like fossils have been placed in this group.

Homogeneous The same throughout. Raspberry jelly is a homogeneous mixture of water flavourings, sugar and gelatin. Raspberry jam is not because of the pips.

Homologous Objects which are similar in basic structure. Homologous chromosomes are similar enough to pair up during meiosis (the cell division that gives rise to sex cells).

Homozygous An organism is said to be homozygous for a particular allele when it has two identical alleles in its genetic makeup. In pea plants the allele for round seed (R) is dominant, the allele for wrinkled seeds is recessive (r). A pea plant which has two dominant alleles for seed shape (RR) in its cells can be described as homozygous dominant (two recessive alleles (rr) make it homozygous recessive).

Hormone A substance, produced in one part of the body, that has its effect somewhere else e.g. antidiuretic hormone is released from part of the brain and has its main effect on the kidneys. The term is now applied only to animals, 'Growth substance' is used for plants. Hormones, like adrenaline, thyroxine, testosterone or oestrogen are fairly small molecules which are secreted by glands directly into the blood stream. The glands have a good blood supply. The hormones get carried around by the blood so that they reach the target organs or tissues where they produce an effect.

Horsepower Power is the rate at which energy can be transferred. It is usually measured in joules per second (i.e. watts). One horsepower should therefore be the rate at which an average, fit horse can work.
This has been taken as being 745.7 joules per second i.e. 745.7 watts.

Hubble constant Used in astronomy.

$$H = \frac{\text{velocity at which galaxy is retreating from us}}{\text{distance between that galaxy and us}}$$

There is some doubt as to whether it is a true constant as its value varies from $1 \cdot 6 \times 10^{-18}$ to $3 \cdot 2 \times 10^{-18}$ s^{-1}. The units seem a bit strange but the constant is given by velocity over distance. We get the velocity of a galaxy by measuring its red shift (see Doppler effect, red shift).

Humidity The amount of water vapour in the air. This is usually given as a percentage of the total water that the air could contain. When the humidity is given as 40% it means that that air (at that temperature) could contain another 60% . This is the most useful way of measuring humidity because it gives us an idea of the drying effect. We use the term **relative humidity** for this. We could also express humidity another way: as the mass of water vapour present in a stated volume of air. The term **absolute humidity** is used for this (usual units: kg per m³).

Humus The dark colour of good garden soil results from the decomposed remains of plants and animals. This dark material is humus. It is a slightly gummy substance that glues together the tiny bits of rock that make up the rest of the soil. Humus particles are charged and so are very important in holding useful minerals and water near the surface where plant roots can reach them. Humus is rich in bacteria, fungi and small arthropods.

- 65 -

Hybrid An organism whose parents were genetically different in some way. The term can be used for mules where the parents belong to different species (horse and donkey), or for a brown eyed child with a blue eyed parent.

Hydrocarbon Organic compounds which are composed only of carbon and hydrogen atoms. Natural gas is a hydrocarbon.

Hydrogen bomb (a fusion bomb) A nuclear device that is able to transfer stunning amounts of energy when heavy hydrogen converts to helium. The main ingredient is a compound of hydrogen (as deuterium). Getting deuterium to fuse to helium requires temperatures of about 80 million °C. This high temperature is generated by detonating a small fission bomb (see fusion bomb, deuterium).

Hydrogen bond A weak attraction that can hold molecules together. The bond exists between hydrogen and certain other atoms on the right of the periodic table. Hydrogen bonds are very important in getting proteins to hold their crumpled shape. They also provide the force that holds the two parts of the DNA molecule together.

A diagram showing how two strands of DNA are held together by hydrogen bonds

hydrogen bonds between the bases.

Hydrogen ion Hydrogen ions are almost never found free as H^+. In water they quickly combine with water molecules to form hydroxonium ions (H_3O^+).

Hydrogen peroxide (H_2O_2) is produced naturally in tissues and, as it is toxic, there are enzymes to change it to oxygen and water. It is used as a bleaching agent and as a disinfectant.

Hydrogenation The process by which hydrogen is added to a substance, usually in the presence of a catalyst and using gaseous hydrogen. It is used to produce margarine from vegetable oils but in addition is very widely used in the industry that works with petroleum and coal.

Hydrolysis (Hydro: of water, lysis: splitting) A reaction between the hydroxonium ion or hydroxyl ion or water and some dissolved substance.

Hydrophobia A dread of water. One of the old names for rabies. Rabid people become dreadfully thirsty but for some reason, when they are offered water to drink, they become overwhelmed with terror and beg for it to be removed. (Rabies is caused by a virus). It is possible to be vaccinated against rabies and to be cured of the condition but the treatment is quite unpleasant.

Hydroponics Growing plants without soil. The roots are immersed in water in which the nutrient minerals and oxygen are kept at optimum levels.

Hydroxonium ion See hydrogen ion above.

Hydrous Containing water (e.g. blue copper sulphate has water of crystallisation).

Hypermetropia Long sight. People with this condition have eyes that are unable to see near objects clearly. The condition can be cured by using convex lenses.

Hypertonic The hypertonic solution has the greater osmotic pressure. Sea water is hypertonic to our blood i.e. if blood in a visking tubing bag is placed in sea water, water will leave the blood until the two concentrations are equal (until they are isotonic). (iso: the same; hyper: above; hypo: below)

Hypotenuse The longest side of a right angled triangle.

Hypothermia A dangerous condition in which the body cools down by a few degrees below the normal temperature. The patient needs careful treatment and fairly gentle warming if they are to survive. They must **not be rubbed** to get them warm or given alcohol.

Hypothesis A suggestion as to how something might work. The hypothesis is very useful in science because, once we have one, we can rig up experiments to test whether the idea is correct or not.

Hypotonic A way of comparing two solutions. The hypotonic solution has the lower osmotic pressure (see hypertonic, isotonic).

Hysteresis At our level this is best explained by using an example so we will look at two magnets. As magnet A spins, its north and south pole keeps passing magnet B. Attraction and repulsion will keep magnet B sliding backwards and forwards but its movement will always lag behind the force that produces the movement. When people use the term hysteresis, they are referring to this lag. Hysteresis gives a measure of the amount that strain (the movement) lags behind stress (the force).

this magnet slides backwards and forwards in the groove

this magnet spins

Iapetus ocean About 500 million years ago the northern parts of Scotland and Ireland were part of Canada and were separated from the rest of the British Isles by the Iapetus Ocean. This ocean closed up and the Atlantic then formed due to yet more continental drift. Before people realised that this had happened it was very difficult to understand the geology of Northern Scotland.

Ice Age Periods of cold that have affected the Earth from time to time. At these times the northern and southern parts of the Earth were covered with ice and very large glaciers. Because so much water was locked up in the ice, the sea levels were much lower at these times. This meant that many rivers change from meandering during the interglacial period to fast running during the glacial periods. These changes have left their marks on the countryside. The weight of the ice depressed the land under it, so that land sank during ice ages and 'sprang back' once the ice melted. The last ice age took place some 10 000 years ago. The reasons for the ice ages are not clear though there have been many suggestions.

Igneous rock These rocks are formed when magma solidifies. Magma is the molten rock that exists at great pressure within the earth at depths greater than 16 km. If the magma solidifies quickly, the crystals will be small as in obsidian and basalt. If it cools slowly crystalline rocks like granite will be produced. Magma which contains gas and is thrown from volcanoes solidifies as pumice.

Ileum Part of the intestine between the stomach and the large intestine. It is where digestion is finally completed and where most of the absorption of digested food takes place. The lining on the inside has a very large surface area. Ducts from the liver and pancreas open into it (see page 9 for a simple diagram).

Immunity An ability to resist the effects of a particular infection. Someone who has had mumps will not get the symptoms again even though the mumps virus may get into their body from time to time. Animals (ourselves and other animals) which have an immunity will have soluble proteins (antibodies) in their blood which react with part of the infective agent and inactivate it (see antibody).

Imprinting The process by which many organisms (particularly birds) learn their identity. E.g. ducklings which see only humans after emerging from the egg will treat humans as though they were other ducks. They can be made to think of a particular human as their mother and are likely to have real problems when they mature as they will not breed with other ducks. Hand-reared male antelope can be dangerous during the breeding season as they will regard humans as competitors who must be attacked. In birds there is definite period when imprinting takes place.

Impulse A signal passing along a nerve. All signals along nerves are of the same size. A strong signal is conveyed by sending many impulses close together.

Inbreeding   Sexual reproduction between closely related individuals e.g. brother and sister or first cousins. All organisms carry recessive alleles that are dangerous (e.g. recessive lethals). When two related individuals breed there is a much bigger chance that the offspring will carry pairs of these recessives and so the offspring have a higher chance of having something wrong with them. Inbreeding can be a real problem for small populations e.g. troops of baboons, and mechanisms exist to ensure that new genes are steadily brought into the group.

Independent assortment   This term is used in genetics when we are following two characteristics through a cross e.g. yellow and green seeds and smooth and wrinkled seeds in pea plants. When gametes are formed the alleles behave independently so that any combination of alleles can occur. Independent assortment is only common when the alleles are on different chromosome pairs. In the case of the pea plants above, the alleles would sort to give 4 gamete types: yellow, smooth; yellow, wrinkled; green, smooth and green wrinkled.

Index fossil   Fossils that can be used as markers of geological strata. The organisms that produced these fossils occurred widely at a particular time in the Earth's history and so they are found in rocks from many different parts of our planet.

Indicator   A substance which allows the progress of a chemical change to be followed. In schools we use them mainly to mark the precise stage when acids are neutralised with a base. Phenolphthalein is colourless in acid solutions, red in alkaline solutions.

Indigenous   Of that area. Wolves and bears were indigenous to England some time ago, Oaks still are.

Induced current   Move a conductor in a magnetic field and a current will flow. This is an induced current i.e. induced by the movement. Currents, small and large, are produced in this way in microphones, generators, transformers & metal skipping ropes.

Induction heating   A way of heating metal. The metal to be melted is in a container surrounded by a changing magnetic field. Eddy currents are induced in the metal and produce the heating. Induction furnaces are used in the steel industry.

Inductor   We know that a current in a coil will produce a magnetic field. As the magnetic field grows, it tends to oppose the current that produced it, i.e. the coil acts to reduce the current. Such a coil is known as an inductor. Inductors are very useful when we need to control the size of an alternating current because inductors do not get hot i.e. there is very little energy transferred to heat (i.e. wasted).

Industrial melanisation   The changing of a whole population of organisms to a darker colour because pollution has darkened the colour of their surroundings. This has been well documented in the case of the peppered moth. Pale versions of these moths were more conspicuous on sooty tree trunks and so were more likely to be eaten by birds. Their genes for pale colour were steadily lost from the population in industrial areas and cities.

Inelastic collision   There is a loss of total kinetic energy during such collisions. The missing kinetic energy will be transferred so that the temperature rises, light is given out or noise is produced.

Inert   Will not react. The noble gases (helium, neon etc) are inert, they do not form compounds readily.

Inertia   The property of an object that keeps it doing whatever it was doing i.e. if it is stationary it needs force to get it moving. If it is moving it needs force to get it to speed up, slow down or change direction. Newton's laws deal with inertia.

Inflorescence   This term is used for the arrangement of flowers on an axis. Biologists use the term flower in a very precise way. For example a daisy 'flower' is not a single flower but a collection of flowers arranged in a special way.

Inorganic chemistry The study of substances of mineral origin. The term is used to make a distinction between the study of substances which are derived from organisms (organic chemistry).

Insecta A class of organisms within the arthropods that includes silvertails, termites, grasshoppers, fleas, bugs, beetles, wasps and many others.

Insecticide There are three main groups of insecticide:
Organophosphates work by interfering with signals sent between nerve cells in the body. They contain mainly phosphorous, carbon and hydrogen.
Organochlorines like DDT are chemically stable and water soluble and so they tend to pass along the food chain and cause problems for predators.
Pyrethroids were originally produced from chrysanthemums but are now made synthetically. They are relatively **indiscriminate** in their action i.e. they kill any arthropod rather than just the pest animal.

Insulator Materials which insulate from heat (plastic, glass etc.) are also good electrical insulators. Insulators are made from materials in which the electrons are very tightly bonded to the nucleus. Heat is conducted in solids largely by the free electrons. These free electrons also are what move when a current flows. Obviously, if the electrons are all tightly bound to the nucleus, there will be no free electrons and so there will be little heat or electrical conduction.

Insulin A small protein produced by the pancreas which brings about many changes in the body. The most noticeable change is that the glucose levels in the blood decrease. Insulin is a hormone (see hormone and glucagon).

Integer A whole number (–62, –9, 1 and 2257 are all examples of integers).

Intercostal Muscles between the ribs that are important during breathing. The external intercostals raise the ribs during breathing in, the internal intercostals lower the ribs when breathing out hard. The natural elasticity of the lungs is enough to force the air out during gentle breathing. Intercostals, diaphragm and abdominal muscles are all involved in ventilation (breathing).

Interference When two wave crests pass through each other there will be an extra large crest during the moment that they coincide. In the same way, two troughs will produce an extra large trough (constructive interference). When a crest coincides with a trough we get destructive interference. Interference is something that happens only to waves.

Interpolation The process of getting intermediate values between the known values (see extrapolation).

Interquartile range A set of scores can be divided into four equal parts. The interquartile range is the group of results that lie between the first and third quartile (see quartile for a simple diagram).

Intrusion An intrusion is a mass of molten rock forced into part of the Earth's crust. Because intrusions involve very hot rocks producing great pressure on their surroundings, the rocks around an intrusion become changed i.e. metamorphosed.

Inverse relationship If one thing gets bigger as something else gets smaller we say that there is an inverse relationship between them e.g. energy received from the fire increases as the distance to the fire decreases (see gravity).

Inverse square law See gravity.

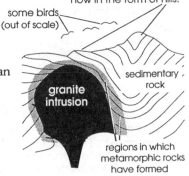

The eroded remains of what was once a large sedimentary deposit now in the form of hills.

some birds (out of scale)

granite intrusion

sedimentary rock

regions in which metamorphic rocks have formed

Ion An electrically charged atom or group of atoms. Cations carry positive charge. Anions carry negative charge. See **bond** for an account of how ions can form and the list of common ions at the end of the book.

Ion exchange A way of removing ions from a solution and replacing them with other ions. Because ions are charged we can get them to stick onto resin beads which carry opposite charge. As an example, we could stick sodium ions on the resin and then, when hard water flows past, the calcium and magnesium ions would stick on and the sodium ions would float free. As sodium ions don't make the water hard we would have changed hard water into soft water. The beads have a very large surface area so that they can carry lots of ions. Such systems are called ion exchange columns. Humus in soils acts as an ion exchange system, holding useful minerals near the surface where plant roots can reach them.

Ionic bond See bond.

Ionisation The process of forming ions. This can happen when radiations (e.g. alpha particles) pass close to atoms. Electrons are dragged from atoms and settles on other atoms (this produces ion pairs). (see bond for other examples of ion formation)

Ionosphere A layer in our atmosphere that extends from 50 km to 1000 km above the surface. The layer is rich in nitrogen and oxygen ions and free electrons. These are produced when radiation from the sun collides with the atoms up there. The ionosphere reflects long and medium radio waves back to the earth so allowing us to send messages to people over the horizon. F.M. radio and television waves pass through so we have to use satellites to get them back to the surface. The nature of the layer changes from day to night.

Iris The pigmented part of the vertebrate eye that controls the amount of light reaching the retina. It has muscles that operate automatically (by reflex). Octopus and squid eyes also have an iris.

Iso The same, as in isosceles: two sides the same length.

Isobar A line on a chart that joins points of equal atmospheric pressure.

Isomer These compounds have the same molecular formula (percentage composition) but different structures and so have different chemical and physical properties. Isomers are very common in organic chemistry because carbon atoms can be joined together in so many different ways.

Isotonic Having the same osmotic pressure i.e. having the same particle concentration (see hypotonic, hypertonic and colligative).

Isotope These are atoms with the same atomic number but different atomic mass. They have the same number of protons in the nucleus but a different number of neutrons. Isotopes have identical chemical properties but different physical properties.

Jejunum A part of the small intestine lying between duodenum and ilium.

Joint Joints can be immovable (e.g. between the cranium bones), partly movable (between the vertebrae) or freely movable (ball and socket joints or hinge joints). Muscles can't push, they can only pull and so joints are worked by pairs of muscles.

Joule The SI unit for energy and work (energy transferred). A joule is the energy transferred when 1 newton is moved through 1 metre. (You do a joule of useful work when you raise an apple by a metre).   4·1868 joules = 1 calorie.

Jugular vein There are 4 jugular veins draining the head (interior and exterior veins on each side which join together to form common jugular veins). Major cuts in the jugular result in sudden massive drop in pressure of the blood supply to the brain so that consciousness is lost within seconds.

Kelp The common name for seaweeds that belong to the group Laminaria (brown algae). They are characterised by having very long fronds and occur in dense beds off those coasts that have cold water offshore.

Kelvin A temperature scale with the same interval size as the Celsius scale but 0K is $-273 \cdot 15°C$ (no degree symbol is used with the kelvin scale).

Keratin A tough protein which forms the main part of hair, nails, horns and the outer part of skin. The protein is rich in sulphur which is why burnt hair smells so awful.

Ketone Organic compound having the general structure shown here. Many organisms produce ketones (ketone bodies) during the breakdown of fats. Ketones have the smell of sour apples and can be smelt on the breath of people with untreated diabetes.

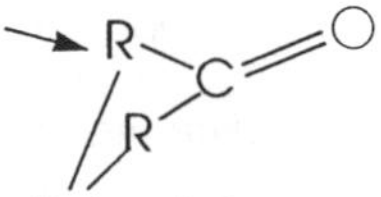

R stands for CH_3 or some other group

Kidney An organ which filters blood. In simple terms there is first filtration under pressure followed by reabsorption of substances useful to the body. It is the main organ for excreting nitrogenous waste (urea, uric acid etc) and for regulating salt concentration (and so osmotic pressure).

A very simple diagram showing the main function of the kidney

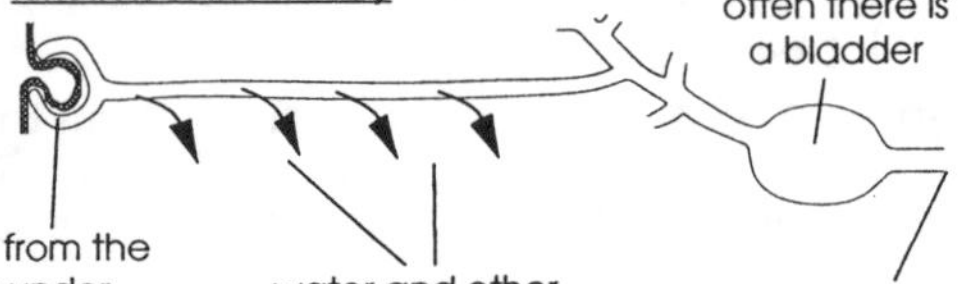

often there is a bladder

filtration from the blood under pressure

water and other useful substances are reabsorbed back into the blood

concentrated waste is expelled

Kilowatt 1000 watts. The watt is used to measure the rate at which energy is transferred:
1 watt = 1 joule per second.

Kinetic theory An explanation for the way that matter behaves. The theory assumes that matter is made of particles and that these particles are in constant motion. This motion becomes more violent as the temperature rises. The theory helps us to explain gas pressure, boiling, the difference between solids, liquids and gases, diffusion and many of the other properties of matter.

Kipp's apparatus A way of producing controllable supplies of any gas that is produced when a liquid acts on a solid. It is often used to give a supply of hydrogen by reacting hydrochloric acid with zinc.

Knocking 1. Mating call of the death watch beetle.
2. The sound made by a petrol engine when the fuel ignites before the piston has reached the top of the compression stroke. It happens when the wrong grade of fuel is used (i.e. low octane fuel in a high performance engine).

Knot A unit of speed used by mariners and aviators. Nautical miles are useful because there are very close to 60 of them per degree of arc on the earths surface.
1 knot = 1 nautical mile per hour $\approx 1 \cdot 15$ statute miles per hour.

Kreb's cycle A sequence of reactions that occur in cells. The reactions are very important in the eventual transfer of energy to ATP (after involving $NADH_2/FADH_2$).

Krypton A noble gas which occurs in our atmosphere (1 part per 670 000).

L.E.D. Light emitting diode.

Labelled compound If we want to see what happens to a particular substance in a reaction we can 'label' its molecules. We can use radioactive atoms to make up the molecules. For example we can supply plant leaves with light and radioactive carbon dioxide. We then see what substances are radioactive at different intervals after the start. In this way we can get some idea of what happens during photosynthesis.

Labile Unstable, easily damaged. Used for substances.

Lactic acid An organic acid which is common in nature. Lactic acid is the main acid in yogurt. It is produced by animals during anaerobic respiration and is one of the causes of fatigue in hard-working muscles. $CH_3CHOHCOOH$ ——

COOH is the acid part

Larva The juvenile stage of many animals. Larvae are able to live independently but are not normally sexually mature. Tadpoles and fly maggots are both examples.

Laser Light amplification by stimulated emission of radiation. An optical laser beam is made up of light in which all the photons are in phase (the wave crests all coincide) and have the same wavelength. The ruby laser consists of a cylinder of ruby, 5 cm long and 1 cm in diameter. The ends are polished so that they are parallel to each other allowing light to bounce back and forth inside the crystal. One end is mirrored, the other end is half-mirrored. By exciting chromium atoms inside the crystal, intense light builds up inside it and eventually emerges as a very dense beam from the half-mirrored end.

Latent heat The energy needed to cause a change of state e.g. change solid iron into liquid iron or water into water vapour. Latent means hidden. The heat is hidden because there is no temperature change even though we keep adding energy. The energy is needed just to free the particles from each other (melting) or to move them further apart (evaporation).

Laurasia The supercontinent that separated from Gondwanaland about 130 million years ago. It was made up of what is now North America, Greenland, Europe & Asia.

Lava The molten material that is extruded onto the surface of the Earth.

Leaf The main photosynthetic organ of plants. They are designed so that carbon dioxide and oxygen can exchange readily and so there is a good supply of water from the soil.

A cross section through part of a leaf

thin cuticle

palisade mesophyll

spongy mesophyll

thin cuticle

stoma — i.e. the hole itself

upper epidermis (no chloroplasts)

cells with many chloroplasts

cells with irregular shapes and fewer chloroplasts

air spaces between the cells

lower epidermis chloroplasts only in the guard cells

Legume Member of the bean, pea, clover, gorse family. They are important in agriculture because of the nitrogen fixing bacteria found in nodules on their roots. Their seeds are rich in protein and so are important in the diet of humans.

Lens A device that causes a beam of rays to converge or diverge. They needn't be made of glass. Magnetic lenses are used in electron microscopy to focus the electron beam.

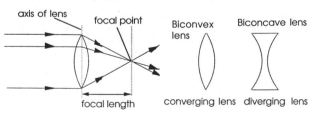

axis of lens

focal point

Biconvex lens

Biconcave lens

focal length

converging lens   diverging lens

Leucocyte   The collective name for all white blood cells. There are two groups:
Agranulocytes: engulf bacteria and are involved in the antihistamine reaction.
Granulocytes: one sub–group engulf bacteria and the other produce antibodies.
(see blood cells for a diagram)

Lichen   A fungus and algae, working together (a symbiotic relationship). The fungi provide a higher humidity and support on what would be a very difficult surface for algae to stick to. The algae supply nutrients for fungal growth.

Life–cycle   The stages in the life of an organism from fertilisation to death. Life–cycles usually include the sort of details that biologists find so interesting e.g. whether the chromosomes in the cells exist as pairs (diploid) or as a set of single chromosomes (haploid).

Typical mammalian life cycle

Vegetative body (2n) — Meiosis — Fertilization — Zygote (2n) — Mitosis — (back to Vegetative body)

Light   The visible part of the electromagnetic spectrum.

Violet	Indigo	Blue	Green	Yellow	Orange	Red
	425 to 445	445 to 500	500 to 575	575 to 585	585 to 620	

390 to 425 nanmetres i.e. $3 \cdot 9$ to $4 \cdot 25 \times 10^{-7}$m

Wavelengths in nanometres

620 to 750 nanmetres i.e. $6 \cdot 2$ to $7 \cdot 5 \times 10^{-7}$m (which can be increased to 900 nanmetres if high power light is used)

Light–year   The distance travelled by light in a vacuum in one year. It is equal to 5.8785×10^{12} miles, or 9.4607×10^{15} metres. The measure is useful in astronomy.

Lightning   A surge of current passing between clouds or between clouds and the Earth. The cloud to earth lightning can involve currents of 10 000 amperes in one direction followed by a return current of about 20 000 amperes in the other. Lightning occurs because a charge difference builds up between cloud and earth or between top and bottom of a cloud.

Limiting factor   The idea of a limiting factor can be understood by considering a growing plant. If it is not growing at its maximum possible rate, something (water supply or available nutrients, light or carbon dioxide) must be in short supply. The factor that is in short supply is the limiting factor. The term is also used in chemistry e.g. when discussing enzyme–catalysed reactions, the **substrate** may be the limiting factor.

Line of best fit   See best fit.

Linnaean system   A method for classifying organisms first devised by Carolus Linnaeus. The groups used are: kingdom, order, class, family, genus and species (see classification and genus).

Lipase   The general name for enzymes that are able to digest lipids. Lipases hydrolyse (split by adding water) lipids into fatty acids and glycerol.

Lipid   A large and varied group of organic compounds composed mainly of carbon and hydrogen. They are very soluble in organic solvents (e.g. benzene, diethyl ether, etc.). The group includes fats, waxes, glycolipids (lipids with glucose), phospholipids (phosphate and lipid) and others. (see also fatty acids)

Lipoprotein   A lipid joined to a protein. They are essential in vertebrate plasma for transporting materials like lipids, triglycerides and cholesterol. These substances can only be moved by attaching them to a water–soluble carrier molecule.

Liquid One of the states of matter in which the particles are held close together but are free to slide over each other. Liquids take the shape of their container. Because the particles in a liquid are already close together, liquids are not very compressible.

Lithosphere The rocks near the surface of the earth. It includes the **sial** (low density rocks rich in silica and alumina), **sima** (higher density rocks rich in silica and magnesium, making up most of the ocean beds) and upper mantle (the layer between the crust and the core).

Litre A unit of volume. **The SI unit of volume is the dm³.** The litre is defined as the volume of 1 kilogramme of water at $4°C$.   1 litre = $1·000\ 028\ dm^3$

Liver In vertebrates it is a large gland with many functions. Its main function is the production of bile which is shed into the intestine. It is involved in the regulation of glucose levels in the blood, in the production of certain blood plasma proteins (albumins, transport lipoproteins and clotting factors). It is very important in detoxification of drugs including alcohol (which is why it is one of the organs badly affected by long-term alcohol abuse, i.e. cirrhosis of the liver) and deactivation of many hormones. Because livers are large and are involved with lots of chemical reactions, they produce a lot of heat. (you should get 5 main functions from this account). Damage to the liver in men means that oestrogens are no longer destroyed as effectively and so the men show increasing feminisation (seen in advanced alcoholics).

Locus In genetics we use this term to indicate a particular position on chromosomes. More formally it is the position on homologous chromosomes that can be occupied by any of several alleles for a particular characteristic. As an example we would always look for the alleles controlling the tall/short condition in pea plants at a certain point (the locus) on a certain chromosome pair.

Logarithmic scale In a logarithmic scale each new interval covers ten times the range of the previous interval. Five consecutive intervals might be: 1, 10, 100, 1000, 10 000. In some graphs the line becomes very steep and quickly disappears off the page. Such a graph can be redrawn using a log scale on one, or both, axes. The graph on the right has the y-axis drawn as a log scale. Both graphs are of the same function.

The curve has become linear

$y = 10^x$

4 (i.e 10000)
3 (i.e. 1000)
2 (i.e. 100)
1 (i.e. 10)

$y = 10^x$

The y axis is set out as a log scale

Logic gate Circuits which perform logic decisions are called logic gates.They are very small and so lots of them can be fitted into a small circuit. They form the basis of modern computers. In the case of the AND gate, a small voltage must be applied to all the inputs (in this case, A and B) before a small voltage will appear at the output (F).

Long sight Individuals with this condition have a cornea which is not really curved enough. Light from close objects is focussed behind the retina. Light from distant objects is focussed on the retina. They see distant objects clearly.

Long sight and its correction

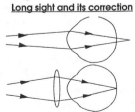

Longitudinal wave Sound waves in a gas give a good example of longitudinal waves. The important thing about these waves is that the vibrating particles are vibrating in the same direction as the direction in which the energy is moving. See also 'transverse waves'. Longitudinal waves will pass through liquids (e.g. shock waves through the centre of the Earth).

We correct long sight by using convex lenses in front of the eyes

Loudness of sound   Human hearing does not register sound in a straight forward way. Two notes with the same energy levels but different pitch will not sound as loud. The decibel system gives a measure of the energy level in sound, and so is useful when sending sound but not so useful when hearing it.
For our ears to detect a change in intensity the new sound must carry about 26% more energy than the previous sound.

Loudspeakers   Moving-coil loudspeakers work because magnetic fields interact. One field is permanent and one field is generated by current from the music centre (amplifier) and so the field changes as the sound signal changes.

Lubricant   These stop the two surfaces coming into contact by coating each surface with a slippery film. Ideally, lubricant molecules should stick tightly to the surface molecules but not stick to each other. Air, oils, grease, graphite are all good lubricants.

Lumen   The space inside a tube or other container e.g. the inside of a kidney tubule or the bladder.

Lung   The organ for gas exchange in air breathing vertebrates. Lungs have a very large surface area that is in contact with the atmosphere and is very well supplied with blood. Air is moved in and out of lungs by muscle systems in the diaphragm and abdomen as well as between the ribs. Lungs are naturally elastic and will collapse (pneumothorax) if air is allowed into the space between the ribs and lungs (pleural space). Many air breathers use a different system for gas exchange e.g. insects have their whole bodies permeated by a system of fine tubules which carry air from the outside to all the tissues. (see also gas exchange, ventilation)

surface of the lung

larynx

a section through part of the lung

bronchiole

trachea

air-sac (alveolus)

main bronchus

capillaries

terminal bronchioles

bronchioles

pleural membrane

Lymph   The clear liquid that escapes from blood capillaries, bathes tissues and then returns to the circulation along a series of tubes. Lymph drains back into the blood system where the pressure is very low i.e. at the large veins close to the heart.

Lymphocyte   See leucocyte and blood cells.

Lysis   Splitting, as in electrolysis; the splitting of substances using an electric current.

Lysosomes   Tiny structures in the cytoplasm of cells that contain digestive enzymes. They can be used to digest material drawn into the cytoplasm e.g. bacteria. They can also digest the cell itself should it become badly damaged or redundant (autolysis). It is everyone's hope that the weapon inventors never find an easy way of triggering lysosomes to autolyse. If they could, soldiers would watch the 'enemy' dissolve in front of their eyes until just skin and bones remained.

Machine   A device for doing work. If a machine uses fuel we call it an engine. Machines can be very simple or quite complex: toothpicks, bottle openers or a crane are all machines.

Macromolecule   Very large molecules which are usually polymers e.g. proteins.

Magma Molten rock that is often filled with gas. Magma is produced at depths greater than 16km and under great pressure. It can be forced to the surface as a lava or forced between layers of existing rock as an intrusion. Igneous rocks originate as magma.

Magnet A metal bar (or coil carrying a current) which will repel (or attract) other magnets if these are brought close to it. The test for magnetism is to see whether the two lumps of metal will repel each other. See also ferromagnetic materials.

Magnetic dip The angle between the line of the Earth's magnetic field and the horizon.

Magnetic domains These are regions within a magnet in which all the atomic magnetic fields (more correctly, the magnetic moments) are arranged in the same direction. Magnetic domains are about 0·1mm to 1 mm across. In a very strong magnet all the magnetic domains would be arranged in the same direction (aligned).

Magnitude The size of something or brightness of a star. An order of magnitude is a change (larger or smaller) by a factor of 10 e.g. from 1 to 10, or 100 to 1000.

Magnox The name used for a certain type of nuclear reactor. These reactors get their name because their uranium fuel is loaded into canisters made from magnesium alloys. Magnox A is magnesium with 0·8% aluminium and 0·01% beryllium.

Malaria A disease that is common in many parts of the developing world. It is caused by a parasite that lives in the red blood cells and liver. The worst form is caused by *Plasmodium falciparum*. The parasite is spread from person to person by certain mosquitoes. Attempts to control malaria aim at killing mosquitoes or at killing parasites. Unfortunately neither approach is simple as both parasite and mosquito have developed resistance to the substances used.

Malpighian tubules The insect's equivalent of the kidney. They differ from kidneys in that the tubule fluid is not produced by pressure filtration but by transport of salts from the 'blood' surrounding the tubule into the tubule lumen. Water will follow.

Malt This is produced by wetting grain (usually barley), keeping it warm while it germinates and then killing it and drying it. During germination many starch digesting enzymes are produced and these can then be used to digest the stored starch to sugars e.g. maltose, that can be used in fermentation to produce beer or other drink.

Mammalia A class of warmblooded vertebrates that are characterised by having hair and secreting milk. The first mammals appeared during the Triassic.

Man *Homo sapiens* Linn. A truly bipedal mammal with an enlarged cranial capacity (about 1300cm^3) and a complex social system.

Mantle This part of the Earth extends from below the crust to a depth of about 2900km below the crust. The mantle is believed to consist of silicate rocks.

Maser These operate in the same way as lasers but produce radiation in the microwave part of the electromagnetic spectrum (from 1mm to 0·3m).

Mass The quantity of matter in a body. The mass of a body determines what its acceleration will be for a given force. The mass of an object does not change if it is moved further away from the earth. Objects in space may be weightless but they are not without mass.

Mass number This is the total number of protons and neutrons in the nucleus of an atom.

Matches A portable device (usually of wood or cardboard) for generating a flame. The active tip usually contains antimony trisulphide, potassium chlorate, sulphur and charcoal. The striking surface contains red phosphorous.

Mean One way of expressing an average. To find the mean of n numbers we add up the numbers and then divide by n. The mean of 3, 5, 5 6, 9, and 11 is 6·5. Care is needed when using means. If the sample size is small or if the numbers are widely scattered the mean may be very misleading. There are 5 people in an office. One has 11 weeks holiday, the others get a week each. The mean is 3 weeks per person.

Median A way of expressing an average. The median is the middle number in a sequence of numbers. There will be two median values whenever there is an even number of numbers.

Medium Many waves travel because the particles in matter are made to vibrate and pass their vibration on to the next lot of particles and so on. E.g. sound waves travel because gas particles vibrate. Without the particles there would be no sound, the particles are the **medium** through which the waves pass. Earthquake waves have earth as the medium. Light waves do not seem to need a medium i.e. they travel well in a vacuum.

Medulla oblongata The part of the brain that controls functions like breathing, heart rate and blood pressure. Serious injury is immediately fatal. The medulla is at the base of the skull just before the start of the spinal chord.

Meiosis During this process a nucleus divides twice to form four nuclei. Each final nucleus contains half the original number of chromosomes (i.e. only one chromosome from each of the chromosome pairs, the cells are **haploid**). This halving of the chromosome number has to happen before fertilisation, otherwise the chromosome number would double with each new generation. It wouldn't take many generations of this before chromosomes would swamp the cells. In meiosis, homologous chromosomes will pair up early in the division. (see also mitosis)

Melting point This is the temperature at which both solid and liquid phases of a substance can exist together. If we increase the pressure the melting point will be lowered and so tables giving standard M.P.s should state the relevant pressure (Normally standard pressure of 101 325 Pa) (1 **pascal** is the pressure due to 1 newton on 1 m^2). Many organic compounds have very precise melting points and these can be used to help identify them.

Membrane Cells have a variety of membranes around and inside them. These membranes play a vital role in regulating the movements of chemicals. Cells in the kidneys, salivary glands and liver, where there is rapid movement of substances have membranes rich in proteins. The proteins play an important part in the membrane's activities. Do bear in mind that the molecules of the membrane are vibrating about all the time. Our whole world is in a **state of flux**, membranes included.

A diagram showing the arrangement of molecules in a membrane

peptide molecule in a pore

protein molecule on the surface

lipid molecules, (glycolipids, phosopholipids and cholesterol).

Mendel's Laws A summary of Mendel's two laws.
Every characteristic of an organism is controlled by a pair of alleles.
One of these may be dominant . If so its effect will appear in the offspring. The other (the recessive) will not show an effect on the offspring i.e. will not be expressed.
Each allele is transmitted from generation to generation as a single, separate, unchanging unit. (continued on the next page)

Mendel's Laws (continued) During meiosis each pair of alleles separates and each gamete receives one of the alleles from each pair of alleles. This is known as the principle of segregation.
When gametes are formed the different alleles act independently. This means that an allele from one pair can be found in a gamete with any other allele. (the principle of independent assortment).
Each organism inherits one allele (for each characteristic) from each parent.

Exceptions have been found to these rules and the rules need to be modified to take account of more recent discoveries. They still apply though when we look at the genetic examples chosen by Mendel.

> Using letters A, a, B, b, to represent 4 different alleles (2 pairs of alleles)
> **The principle of segregation**
> Any gamete (e.g. ovum) could have A or a, it could not have both A and a.
> **The principle of independent assortment**
> The alleles are allocated to the gametes independently i.e. considering these two pairs of alleles we could have the following gametes AB, Ab, aB, ab. Any one allele can be found with either allele from a different pair.

Meninges Three membranes that cover the surface of the central nervous system in vertebrates. They have a good blood supply. Meningitis is an infection of these layers.

Menstrual cycle The sequence of egg production, preparation of the uterus for pregnancy, the removal of the outer lining of the uterus with a discharge of blood and then egg production again. Only the old world primates have a menstrual cycle.

| menstrual period lasts about 5 days | lining in the uterus is now being replaced | egg is released on about day 14 | uterus lining is now ready to receive the fertilised egg | if no fertilisation, the cycle starts again |

0 1 2 3 4 5 6 7 8 9 10 11 12 13 **14** 15 16 17 18 19 20 21 22 23 24 25 26 27 28

days after the start of the cycle

The cycle can be interrupted when an egg becomes fertilised, so no more eggs are produced during the pregnancy. The cycle works because of controls by negative feedback e.g. rising levels of oestrogen in the blood inhibit the release of the very substance that is stimulating oestrogen production.

Mensuration The measurement of lengths, areas and volumes.

Meristem Regions of active cell division in plants. Growth in plants occurs because cell division (mitosis) is followed by elongation. Roots and shoots have meristems at the growing points (apical meristems). The stems of plants increase in girth (circumference), the cell division for this takes place in a layer between the woody part of the stem and the outer parts. This layer is referred to as cambium (see also phloem).

Mesophyll Tissue inside the leaf. The mesophyll cells contain the green pigments responsible for photosynthesis (chlorophylls). (see leaf for a diagram)

Messenger RNA Single stranded RNA that is made in the nucleus and then diffuses out to the cytoplasm to those places where protein are synthesised. These molecules carry genetic information from nucleus to cytoplasm. Do remember that genes produce their first effect (express themselves) in the form proteins.

Metabolism This is now used to refer to all the chemical processes going on in an organism. This includes the processes in which new tissue is laid down (anabolism), and those in which molecules are broken down during respiration etc (catabolism). The basal metabolic rate is the level of chemical activity in the resting organism. The easiest way to measure this is to record the rate of oxygen consumption.

Metabolite Any substance that is involved in reactions taking place in an organism e.g. carbon dioxide in plants, glucose, amino acids.

Metal This is a general term for elements which have the following properties:
1. they have a characteristic lustrous (shiny) appearance
2. they are good conductors of heat and electricity
3. They can be bent without breaking i.e. they are malleable.
3. metals form positive ions (cations).
Those elements which are placed at the junction between metals and non–metals on the periodic table, may show some metallic and some non-metallic properties e.g. the semiconductors used in electronics (see periodic table for a diagram).

Metallic bond See bond.

Metamorphic rock Metamorphic rocks are produced by the action of heat and pressure on other rocks. These rocks have been changed from their original state by a process like mountain building and the intrusion or extrusion of magma. Slate, marble and gneiss are metamorphic rocks.

Degree of change	Sandstone	Limestone	Mudstone	Clay	Basic lava
Low	quartzite	marble	slate	slate	greenstone
Medium	quartzite	marble	mica schist	amphibolite*	amphibolite
High	quartzite	marble	gneiss	amphibolite	amphibolite

* amphibolites are a group of rocks rich in iron, magnesium and silica (e.g. hornblende)

Metaphase The stage in cell division at which the chromosomes have become visible and group together around the equatorial plate (see mitosis and meiosis).

Metastasis This is the movement of malignant cells (or infective agents like bacteria) away from the first region of multiplication. In the case of skin cancers, the first symptoms, darkened mole–like regions on the skin, are fairly easily treated by removing the affected tissue. After metastasis the condition is very hard to treat successfully as the cancerous cells have spread widely and can't be treated surgically.

Meteorite A solid object from outer space. They range in size from pea–sized (which cause shooting stars) to lumps of 100 tons or more. The Earth is bombarded by about a million meteors each day which adds about 10 tons of matter per day. Certain governments are now taking more seriously the chance that we will be struck by a very large meteorite at some stage and have begun scanning space for these.

Methanol A very poisonous alcohol (CH_3OH). Methanol is changed (metabolised) to formic acid in the body. Formic acid is very toxic.

Methane (CH_4) A flammable gas produced by decaying organic matter or in coal mines.

Metric measurements The system that uses metres, grams and decimetres cubed.

Microbe Any microscopic organism. The term is used in a general way to include malaria parasites (small animals), cholera bacillus, flu virus, soil bacteria etc. It is a much better term than 'bug' or 'germ'. These two terms are altogether too vague to be useful in science.

Microphone Equipment that converts sound waves into an electrical signal.

Microscope The compound light microscope allows us to get a much enlarged view of the specimen. The specimen needs careful preparation, tissues must be held firmly so that is does not distort, thinly sliced and stained. Using visible light we can get a useful magnification of about 1500 x. Lenses can be combined to give higher magnifications but no more detail is added (the blobs just become larger blobs, see resolving power for a diagram). To improve resolution we need to use shorter wavelengths. As ultraviolet has shorter wavelengths than visible light people made special microscopes that used UV. Later they built microscopes that used beams of electrons in a vacuum. In the case of the electron microscope, magnetic lenses are used to produce useful enlargements of about 200 000 x. Great care is taken to make sure that the process of specimen preparation does not affect the very thing we want to study (such distortions are known as artifacts).

Microtome Equipment used to prepare very thin slices of specimen for viewing under the microscope. The specimens can be frozen before slicing. They can also be embedded in paraffin wax and sliced for the light microscope, or embedded in synthetic resin and sliced for the electron microscope (much thinner slices are possible using resin).

Microwave Electromagnetic radiation (i.e. like light or radio waves) with wavelengths ranging from 1 mm to 30 cm .Microwaves fit in between infra red and very short radio waves. They can be used for radar or heating food.

Milky way The greater part of our galaxy as seen from Earth.

Millon's test A test for protein. As mercury salts are present in the solution the test is not used much in schools. The solution contains mercury nitrate and nitrite.
Add 2 cm^3 of the test solution to a test tube. Add 1 cm^3 of Millon's reagent and boil. A white precipitate forms which coagulates on heating and turns red or salmon pink.

Mineral A natural inorganic substance that has a definite chemical composition and is almost always in a crystalline form. Ice is regarded as a mineral but coal and oil are not because they are organic in origin.

Mirror A polished surface which is effective at reflecting light. Mirrors reflect the light in a way that allows images to be formed (white paper reflects much of light falling on it but it is not a mirror). Curved mirrors will act as magnifiers (or 'reducers'). These curved mirrors are used in large telescopes (glass lenses would just be too heavy) and in long lenses for cameras. Such telescopes are known as reflector telescopes.

Mirror image The reversed image seen in a mirror in which the right side is where the left side should be etc. If we were faced by an identical clone of ourselves we would expect their left hand to be opposite our right hand.

Misleading charts People can present their figures in such a way that we can be mislead. The graph on the left seems to suggest that the population is doubling each year. The jagged part of the y axis for the graph on the right alerts us to the fact that the scale does not start at zero.

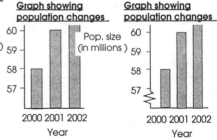

Missing mass See dark matter.

Mitochondria Small objects scattered through the cytoplasm of most eukarytic cells. They are surrounded by a membrane with a definite internal arrangement of membranes. Enzyme systems in the mitochondria are involved in transferring energy from small molecules to ATP. Mitochondria have their own DNA and are believed to have originated when bacteria invaded nucleated cells.

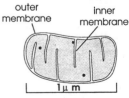

Mitosis This type of cell division is responsible for growth and repair. Mitosis produces daughter cells which are genetically identical to the parent cell. Strictly speaking, the term applies to the division of the nucleus, 'cytokinesis' is the term used for the division of the cytoplasm.

A diagram showing the main stages of mitosis

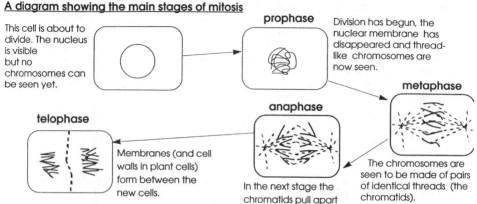

This cell is about to divide. The nucleus is visible but no chromosomes can be seen yet.

prophase Division has begun, the nuclear membrane has disappeared and thread-like chromosomes are now seen.

metaphase

telophase

anaphase

Membranes (and cell walls in plant cells) form between the new cells.

In the next stage the chromatids pull apart

The chromosomes are seen to be made of pairs of identical threads (the chromatids).

Mitral valve The valve between the left atrium and left ventricle in the hearts of mammals and birds. The valve is made from two tough flaps which are attached at the junction between the atrium and ventricle. They are prevented from collapsing the wrong way by a tendon which is attached to the bottom of the ventricle. Blood flows from atria to ventricles.

Mixture A mixture has the properties of the substances in it, it can be separated by simple physical methods (filtering, sieving, distillation etc.) and no reaction takes place when mixtures are made.

Mixture	Compound
e.g. iron filings mixed with sand	e.g. glucose , table salt
1. The different substances in the mixture can be separated by simple physical means e.g. use a magnet.	1. The elements in it cannot be separated by simple physical means, e.g. it isn't a simple matter to separate table salt into chlorine gas and sodium.
2. The properties of the mixture are the same as those we expect from all the individual substances in it, e.g. Its colour, density and smell will be in the same proportion as they occur in the ingredients.	2. The properties of the compound are different from the elements in it, e.g. carbon, oxygen and hydrogen are very different from glucose.
3. Energy is **not** given out or absorbed when the mixture is made.	3. Some energy changes occur when compounds are formed. The energy is usually given out or absorbed.
4. The composition of the mixture can be changed because the ingredients need not be present in any particular proportion.	4. The elements in the compound **always** combine in very definite proportions by weight, e.g. in a glucose molecule there are always 6 carbon, 6 oxygen and 12 hydrogen atoms.

Modal class A term used in statistics to refer to the group that contains the most results.

Moderator e.g. graphite or heavy water are used in nuclear reactors to slow down the neutrons. Slower neutrons have a much greater chance of causing another disintegration in the fuel. The moderator surrounds the fuel elements.

Modulation This occurs when we impose one wave form onto another wave (the **carrier wave**). Amplitude modulation (**A M**) is used for commercial broadcasts of the long, medium and short wavelengths. With FM it is the frequency that is modulated.

carrier wave   modulated carrier wave

Mohorovicic discontinuity (Moho) The boundary between the crust and the mantle. It marks a change in the rock densities and occurs at about 35 km below the continents.

Molality The number of moles of solute added to and dissolved in a dm³ **of solvent. N.B. it is not the same as molarity.**

Molarity The concentration of a solution given as the number of moles of solute in 1 dm³ of solution.

Molar solution A solution with a concentration of one mole per dm³.

Mole The amount of a substance which contains 6.023×10^{23} molecules, atoms or ions. The atomic mass (or formula mass) of any substance expressed as grammes, gives us a mole of that substance.

e.g.1 If we need a mole of powdered iron, we look up the atomic mass of iron and then we weigh out that amount of iron powder in grammes.

e.g.2 If we need 0.5 moles of NaCl we calculate the formula mass of the NaCl (i.e. $23 + 35.5 = 58.5$). Multiply the result by 0.5 and then weigh out 29·25 g. of NaCl.

Molecule Molecules form when electrons are shared between atoms. Starch, amino acids, water, O_2 in oxygen gas etc. all exist as molecules. Molecules are held together because of covalent bonding. It may help to consider ions here. In an ionic compound (e.g. KCl), the electrons are not shared, the cation (K^+) has lost an electron and the anion (Cl^-) has gained one.

Moment A moment is a turning force. In simple terms it is given by force times distance. In the diagram on the right the moment = force A x distance B (Strictly, the distance we use is the distance between the line of the force and the fulcrum as shown in the lower diagram).

Two diagrams showing the measurements needed to calculate moments

force

force A distance B dist.

Momentum Momentum = mass x velocity (units kgms⁻¹) Momentum is the property of matter that makes it hard to speed it up or slow it down or change the direction of travel. We take it as an unbreakable rule that momentum is always conserved during a collision (this is certainly not true of kinetic energy, some of the energy can be transferred to heat or light or sound as happens during an inelastic collision).

force

line of force

distance   d

Monomer Small molecules which can be joined together to make long chains e.g. glucose molecules join to make starch, glycogen, cellulose or insect chitin, amino acids join together to make protein.

Monosaccharide Sugars like glucose ($C_6H_{12}O_6$) or ribose ($C_5H_{10}O_5$). Monosaccharides can be joined together to form molecules like starch or glycogen (**polysaccharides**).

Morphine Morphine is derived from opium poppy sap. It is a very effective pain killer but has side effects; namely, it strongly suppresses ventilation so that breathing slows down and may threaten the life of the patient.
Morphine–like substances (endorphins) are released in our brains during exercise and are responsible for the relaxed feeling of well being that often follows exertion. (see also heroin)

Mucoprotein A protein in which the molecules are linked to a carbohydrate group.

Multiple The product of a given number and some factor
e.g. some multiples of 6 are: 6 (6 x 1),   12 (6 x 2),   18 (6 x 3),   24 (6 x 4) etc.

Muscle Cells which can contract, usually as a result of nerve signals.
Striated muscle (voluntary muscle) is the muscle that moves bones. Each muscle fibre is made of many cells that have fused together to form long fibrils. Such muscle is stimulated to contract by signals from nerve endings.
Cardiac muscle has muscle fibres which are formed from single cells. These fibres branch and join with other fibres. It is found only in the heart. Cardiac muscle is able to contract rhythmically on its own, but its rate of contraction is normally controlled from the brain, taking account of the amount of work that is being done by the animal. **Smooth muscle** (involuntary muscle) is composed of collections of spindle shaped cells. Smooth muscle is responsible for peristaltic contractions of the intestine and ureter and for the control of blood pressure.

Muscles contract because fibres in them slide over each other. This sliding needs a supply of energy and so fit muscle cells have stores of glycogen as well as the good blood supply needed to bring oxygen and glucose and remove carbon dioxide and metabolites. (See also actin and myosin).

Diagrams of a short length of muscle fibre showing filaments

Extended state

Thicker myosin rods

actin filaments

contracted state

z line

Mustard gas A poisonous gas with a slight smell of garlic. It causes mutation by reacting with DNA in cells. It is rapidly decomposed by bleaching powder. (Mustard gas = dichloro–diethyl sulphide $C_4H_8Cl_2S$)

Mutagen Substance or physical effect (e.g.ionising radiation) that brings about changes in the way the genes are expressed e.g. mustard gas, colchicine, dioxin.

Mutation Alterations in the genetic material which can result in changes in the cell or virus. If mutations occur in the cells that produce eggs or sperm they can affect future generations. (see also point mutations).
Point mutations affect a particular part of the DNA chain (say a single triplet code) and so cause changes in the protein produced.
Macromutations occur because of changes to whole chromosomes or parts of chromosomes. There may be extra bits of chromosome, bits missing or bits that have changed places on the chromosome. Many genes are affected in the way that they express themselves by the genes along side them, so changing the order can bring about changes in phenotype even though the DNA is still as before.

Mycelium Thread–like fungal growth. Mycelium forms the vegetative part of many fungi and will eventually give rise to the spore producing structures e.g. the mushroom caps that we sometimes eat.

Mycology The study of fungi.

Myopia Short sight. The cornea is strongly curved so that light from distant objects is focussed before the retina and the image on the retina is not clear. We correct short sight by using diverging lenses (thinner in the middle than the edges).

Myosin See muscle above (see also actin and actomysin).

Natural selection Natural selection is believed to be the basic mechanism that drives evolution. Consider that a pair of blackbirds may have two broods a year with four chicks per brood. If the population is stable and the parents die after three years they will leave a pair of offspring to carry on. 22 offspring will have died and 2 will have survived. The two that survive will have been ' naturally selected '. This mechanism ensures that certain genes remain in a population of organisms while others are lost from the population. It was suggested by Darwin and by Wallace that the organisms most likely to survive natural selection would be those that were best suited to their environment.

Nautical mile The international nautical mile is 1·15078 miles. We use nautical miles in navigation because there are 60 nautical miles in an arc of one degree on the Earth's surface. (A sixtieth of a degree is called a minute i.e. 60 minutes = 1°).

Nebula The term is used in astronomy for luminous patches seen in the night sky. They are composed of other galaxies or of clouds of material from which galaxies are formed. In English nebula means not clearly defined.

Necrosis Death. Has a medical use when describing parts of the body that have died because of lack of oxygen, disease etc.

Negative feedback These are used to control the size of any fluctuations e.g. changes in the speed of a steam engine, the levels of glucose in the blood of mammals. Homeostasis is the name given to control in living systems by means of negative feedback. Consider the regulation of temperature:

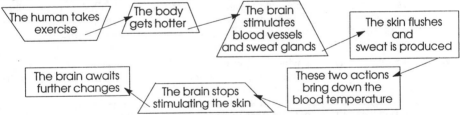

Product feedback in which the final product inhibits the whole production is a common method of controlling the rates of production from biochemical pathways.

Nerve fibre An axon of a nerve cell complete with its myelin sheath when this is present. Axon diameter varies from 1 – 20µm in vertebrates but can be as large as 1 mm in some invertebrates. (see also axon, ganglion).

<u>cross section of an axon with myelin sheath</u>

schwann cell

axon

myelin sheath

Neurone Specialised cells within the nervous system which can conduct impulses. They can convey sensory information to the central part of the system, convey motor signals (signals to muscles) and they form the active part of the central processing part of any nervous system.

(there is a diagram of a motor neurone on the next page)

<u>A diagram showing the main features of a sensory neurone</u>

direction of nerve impulse

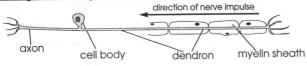

axon

cell body

dendron

myelin sheath

(continued from p. 83)

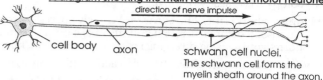

A diagram showing the main features of a motor neurone

direction of nerve impulse

cell body · axon · schwann cell nuclei.
The schwann cell forms the myelin sheath around the axon.

Neutral 1. Having neither positive nor negative charge. This could be because there is no charge at all, but more often it is because there are equal numbers of positive and negative charges.
2. Having pH 7, neither acid nor alkaline. It applies to aqueous solutions in which there are as many hydrogen ions as hydroxide ions.

Neutralisation Adding acid to alkali (or alkali to acid) until the solution consists only of a salt and water. (The end point is rarely 7 though. In the case of ethanoic acid + NaOH the end point is about pH8)   A word equation for this would be:

$$acid \ + \ alkali \longrightarrow salt \ + \ water$$

Newton A unit of force which is defined in the SI system as the force needed to give a mass of 1 kg an acceleration of 1 ms^{-1} .

Newton's laws Three fundamental laws of motion:
1. A body will remain at rest or continue with constant motion unless acted on by a force.
2. The rate of change of linear momentum is proportional to the force applied
    i.e. $F = ma$
3. For every action there is an equal and opposite reaction.

Newtonian mechanics Newton's laws (given above) only work for objects travelling at ordinary speeds. As the speed of objects approach the speed of light, the theory of relativity has to be taken into account and we must use relativistic mechanics e.g. the mass of objects increases as they speed up to the speed of light. Time will also change (it slows down as speed increases) and the calculations must allow for this. Relativistic mechanics are important for calculations involving atomic and subatomic particles.

Niche A way of 'earning a living' within a community. It involves a source of food and a particular way of getting that food, as well being able to compete for breeding sites etc. No two different species can occupy the same niche for any length of time for they are in direct competition and so in time, one species must dominate. Our red squirrel has lost out against the American grey squirrel as they both occupy the same niche and the American squirrel breeds faster and has other advantages.

Nicotine An oily liquid alkaloid found in tobacco leaves. It is highly toxic and is used as a stimulant for people and as an insecticide by people ($C_{10}H_{14}N_2$).

Nitrates Salts made from nitric acid (HNO_3). All metal nitrates are water soluble.

Nitric acid HNO_3

Nitrification The conversion of ammonium ions (NH_4^+) to nitrite and nitrate ions. This change is performed by soil bacteria (Nitrosomonas spp. and Nitrobacter spp.). The nitrate ions produced provide plants with their main source of nitrogen in a form they can absorb.

- 85 -

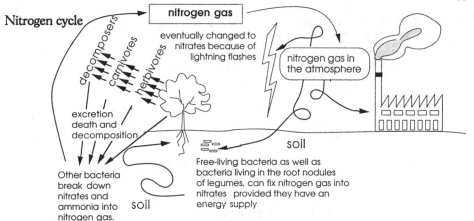

Nitrogen cycle

nitrogen gas

eventually changed to
nitrates because of
lightning flashes

nitrogen gas in
the atmosphere

decomposers
carnivores
herbivores

excretion
death and
decomposition

Other bacteria
break down
nitrates and
ammonia into   soil
nitrogen gas.

soil

Free-living bacteria as well as
bacteria living in the root nodules
of legumes, can fix nitrogen gas into
nitrates provided they have an
energy supply

Nitrogen is an essential part of the chemical that carries the genetic information, (**deoxyribonucleic acid** D N A), and of **proteins**, and so all plants and animals have nitrogen atoms as part of their structure. Most organisms cannot use nitrogen gas directly. Plants have to absorb their nitrogen in the form of nitrates, ammonia or nitrites. Herbivores have to get their nitrogen by eating plants (e.g. as plant protein). The concentration of nitrate in the soil will therefore be one of the factors that decides just how many organisms can inhabit a particular area.

Nitrogen fixation   Certain bacteria and blue-green algae in the soil are able to take in atmospheric nitrogen (nitrogen gas) and change it to ammonia which is then changed to nitrates. These nitrates are essential for plant growth (see also nitrogen).

Nitrogen oxides   Generally referred to as NO_x. There are 6 of these but we need only bother with 2: Nitrogen oxide (nitric oxide, NO) and Nitrogen dioxide (NO_2). These gases can be produced in motor engines because the temperatures in the combustion chamber are high enough to cause any free nitrogen and oxygen to react. The NO_2 reacts with water in the atmosphere producing nitric acid which contributes to the acidity of acid rain (adding to the acidity produced by SO_2).

NO_x   A general formula for nitrogen oxide.
The x stands any number of oxygens e.g. N_2O, NO, NO_2.

Noble gases   Helium, neon, argon, krypton, xenon and radon. All are found in the atmosphere and all are very unreactive but Xe (and to a lesser extent Kr and Rn) will form compounds. The term noble is one of the last examples of emotive words still used in science (base is another).

Noble metals   Silver, gold and platinum and other similar metals that do not corrode i.e. that are not very reactive.

Noise   Signals that are not part of the message. Noise on the radio is made up of all sounds received by the listener that were not made in the studio i.e. atmospherics and hiss and crackle from the equipment. In photography the grain on the film is ' noise'. In everyday life, noise is sound that we don't like.

Non-ferrous metal   Any metals other than iron or steel.

Non-polar compound   These have molecules which are usually uncharged (or if charged, the charge is evenly spread over the surface i.e. there is no dipole moment. Non-polar compounds are not very soluble in water. (see dipole).

Normal   A line which is perpendicular to a plane surface at a particular point (see reflection for a diagram showing a normal).

Not gate   A NOT gate is an inverting gate. You get out whatever you are not putting in. (e.g. no voltage at A and there will be a voltage at the out lead).

A — NOT ▷ → out

$F = \bar{A}$ (F equals not A)

Normal solution This term is now obsolete but you might come across it. A normal solution contains a mole of solute per litre of solution Symbol N, 2N etc.

Nuclear fission Fission is another word for 'splitting', so nuclear fission means the splitting of nuclei. When this occurs, a nucleus splits into smaller nuclei and energy is released. This process involves the heavier elements like uranium or plutonium. Nuclear fission, under control, provides the energy in nuclear power stations.

Nuclear fusion A nuclear reaction that occurs between nuclei of light atoms which produces a heavier atom with the release of energy. Fusion occurs inside the exploding **hydrogen bomb** (and inside our sun) with hydrogen atoms joining together to form helium and releasing huge amounts of energy.
Much effort and money is now being spent in trying to get the fusion reaction to occur under controlled conditions so that it can be used in power stations. These fusion reactions could be between two hydrogen atoms, between hydrogen and helium atoms, between lithium and helium atoms or between lithium and hydrogen atoms. The main difficulty arises from the high temperatures needed to get the fusion to take place, the container walls keep melting.

Nuclear fuel It is the substance that undergoes fission or fusion in a reactor, nuclear bomb or star e.g. enriched uranium, plutonium or heavy hydrogen. Strictly speaking these are not fuels, as true fuels burn whereas in nuclear fuels matter is changed to energy.

Nuclear reactors When a uranium–235 atom disintegrates inside a large lump of uranium, the 3 neutrons are very likely to collide with 3 other atoms before they can escape from the lump. These 3 atoms then disintegrate and release 9 neutrons which collide with more atoms so that up to 27 neutrons are released and so on ! All this happens within millionths of a second so that, in a flash, most uranium atoms disintegrate almost instantly, releasing huge amounts of energy. By using boron control rods and smaller pieces of uranium we can adjust the rate at which the heat is released, i.e. we have a controllable heat source which can be used to boil water, make steam, drive turbines, spin generators, and so produce electricity. (continued on the next page)

<u>**The main components of a gas-cooled reactor**</u>

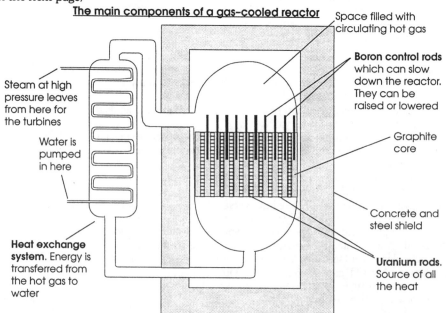

Space filled with circulating hot gas

Steam at high pressure leaves from here for the turbines

Water is pumped in here

Boron control rods which can slow down the reactor. They can be raised or lowered

Graphite core

Concrete and steel shield

Heat exchange system. Energy is transferred from the hot gas to water

Uranium rods. Source of all the heat

Nuclear reactors (continued from the last page) The fast breeder reactor gets its name because the neutrons travel much faster (it uses less moderator) and 'breeder' because it is able to change ordinary uranium into plutonium which is then used as its fuel. The core is much hotter (7500°C) and liquid metal is used as the coolant (usually liquid sodium) (see also cold fusion).

Nuclear waste Radioactive waste can be very dangerous. We detect radiation with special equipment but can't see or smell it and so we have to rely on scientific research institutions and governments to behave responsibly. Governments have not always behaved well. In fact they have often behaved extremely badly.

High level waste (e.g. spent nuclear fuel rods) need to be stored for decades while the last of the very high energy radiation decays away. These wastes can then be re-processed to extract useful materials and the remaining radioactive material put into storage. **Intermediate level waste** (e.g. reactor parts that were close to the core) are mixed with concrete in steel drums and stored.

Low level waste is placed in steel drums in concrete-lined trenches. People feel very uneasy about nuclear waste because the radioactivity lasts for so long. In that time the containers might decay, releasing radioactivity into the ground water and this might be pumped to the homes of our great great grand children.

Nucleic acid See DNA, hydrogen bond (for a diagram) and codon.

Nucleolus Bodies visible in the nuclei of cells. They may take up to 25% of the nucleus' volume. There is strong evidence that they play an important part in the construction of ribosomes, the places where protein is synthesised in the cytoplasm.

Nucleus 1. Of atoms: The positively charged core of an atom. All nuclei contain protons, and apart from hydrogen, all contain neutrons. Electrons, protons and neutrons are very small. If an atom of uranium was the size of an average bedroom, the nucleus would be the size of the full stop at the end of this sentence. The 92 electrons would be a few thousand times smaller. Matter is mostly empty space.
2. Of biological cells: A central part of the cell that has a very important role in expressing the genes. They are easily seen under the microscope because there is a membrane around them. Nuclei contain the chromosomes (DNA and protein) as well as much of the material used when proteins are synthesised. Remember that genes are first expressed by synthesising proteins.
Cells which have a nucleus are known as **eukaryotic**. Bacterial cells have the genetic material free in the cytoplasm, they are **prokaryotic**.

Objective lens The lens of a compound microscope that is closest to the object.

Objective See page 3.

Obtuse angle An angle that is greater than 90° but less than 180°.

Odd-odd nucleus A nucleus that contains an odd number of both protons and neutrons.

Oedema Swelling of tissue due to water retention. The pot bellies of starving children are caused when there is not enough protein in the diet. Blood protein molecules are too large to escape into the tissues from the vessels. They raise the osmotic pressure of the blood so water is drawn back from tissues as the blood leaves the capillaries. When the blood is short of these molecules because of famine or damage to the liver (where they are produced) oedema will result.

Oestrogens Steroid hormones which, together with progesterones, are important in the reproductive cycle in female mammals. Egg production is halted when blood oestrogen levels are high. High levels of oestrogen and progesterone produce a number of other effects: 1. development of mammary glands, 2. changes in the uterus lining, 3. flattening and widening of pelvic girdle. Oestrogens are produced by ovaries after ovulation and by other tissues during pregnancy.

Oil shale & oil sands Mineral oil can be extracted from these by heat treatment. The process is expensive and could change the appearance of the region (very large volumes need to be processed).

Omnivore Animals which eat both plant and animal material in their diet.

Oncogenic Causing cancer. This could be chemical e.g. mustard gas, physical e.g. radiation or viral e.g. the cervical cancer virus.

Opaque Will not let light or other wave motion pass. The plastic tubes which doctors sometimes have to insert in blood vessels have x–ray opaque tips so that the position of the tip will show up on the X-ray.

Operation Maths: The process of carrying out rules of procedure for combining numbers (or symbols). Adding, subtracting, multiplying and dividing are operations.

Optical maser See laser.

Optic fibre See fibre optics.

Optic nerve The nerve that carries signals from the eye (retina) to the brain. The optic nerve (and retina) is an extension of the brain rather than true nerve.

Or gate In a circuit with an OR gate, a current will only flow when there is a voltage at either A or B (or at both).

$$F = A + B \quad (F \text{ equals } A \text{ or } B)$$

Oral contraceptive (the pill) A chemical method for preventing pregnancy used by women. These contain oestrogens and progesterones in various proportions and work by inhibiting egg production. There are side effects so that the method does not suit all women (changes in breasts and distribution of body fat as well as attacks of nausea and an increased chance of blood clots, thrombosis).

Order Order of magnitude, a magnitude expressed to the nearest power of ten (see also entropy).

Ore A mineral deposit in which the metal content is high enough to make it worth mining.

Organ Organs contain at least two tissue types which work together to perform some function in the organism. Skin, heart, brain, kidney and liver are all examples of organs. Like 'beard' (at what point does fuzz on the chin become a beard?), organ is one of those words for which the boundaries may be difficult to define e.g. the stomach is an organ, but then so is the whole alimentary tract.

Organelle The parts of a cell which can be seen as separate objects e.g. mitochondria, chloroplasts, nucleus, endoplasmic reticulum, lysosomes, golgi apparatus.

Organic compound Organic chemistry is the study of the **compounds of carbon**. Until the early part of the last century, people thought that there was something special about the chemicals that are found in living tissue. They felt that these chemicals must possess some 'vital force' which allowed organisms to be alive. Because of this belief a big distinction was made between inorganic and organic chemistry. The most common elements that combine with carbon are hydrogen, oxygen, nitrogen, sulphur, and phosphorus.
Covalent bonds are the most common type of bond in organic compounds.

Oscilloscope The **cathode ray oscilloscope** is the most usual type. Oscilloscopes provide a way of showing how voltage is changing. They respond very rapidly and so can be used to see what is happening in minute intervals of time e.g. thousandths of a second. Any repetitive process which can be changed to an electrical signal can be studied with an oscilloscope. They are therefore used to study nerve signals, muscle twitches, heart beats, brain activity, sound, light and a thousand other processes.

Osmoregulation Controlling the concentration of solutes and water within the bodies of animals. As an example, consider freshwater protozoans which have higher salt content than the water surrounding them. Water will therefore be entering them all the time and will need to be pumped out (they do this by means of contractile vacuoles). Humans control their water content: they excrete concentrated urine when water is short and dilute urine when water is plentiful.

Osmosis The net movement of water across a selectively permeable membrane like 'visking' tubing or the cell membrane. The overall movement will always be away from the region where the water concentration is highest i.e. into the 'saltier' region. Water will continue to move until the concentrations are the same on both sides or until a pressure builds up on one side (It is this sort of pressure that makes lettuce or carrots crisp). (see also water potential)

Ovum Unfertilised egg cell. Once fertilised it is referred to as a zygote.

Oxygen cycle The diagram has been simplified to show one animal and one plant. The full diagram ought to show decomposers and many animals and plants.
It should also show the burning of **fossil fuels** producing carbon dioxide as happens in industry and transport.

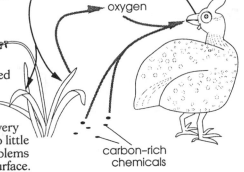

Ozone O_3. Three oxygen atoms combined to form a molecule. It is a   powerful oxidising agent. Too much ozone close to the Earth's surface causes problems because it is so reactive. It is very irritating to our respiratory systems. Too little in the   upper atmosphere causes problems because more UV can then reach the surface.

Ozone layer A layer of ozone some 15 to 50 km above the Earth's surface. The ozone forms there when oxygen is bombarded by radiation from the sun. The ozone is also breaking down back to O_2 so a state of dynamic equilibrium results in which ozone is produced as fast as it is breaking down. The ozone layer is important for life on Earth because it absorbs much of the UV arriving from the sun. Unfortunately human activity (release of chlorine based molecules and high altitude NO_x from car exhausts) have undermined the ozone layer. UV is a mutagen and will have a damaging effect on plants and animals.

PVC Polyvinylchloride. A soft plastic such as is used for the containers of washing up liquid.

Pacemaker A region in the vertebrate heart that keeps generating a signal which stimulates heart muscle to contract. In mammals it is in the right atrium. The signals from the pacemaker can be modified by signals from the brain so that the heart can beat faster or slower as needed.

Pancreas A gland found in vertebrates which secretes enzymes and sodium hydrogen carbonate into the small intestine. It also secretes hormones into the blood stream (insulin and glucagon).

Pangaea A supercontinent that survived for 200 million years until the beginning of the jurassic (age of the dinosaurs) when it broke up into Laurasia and Gondwanaland).

Paper Paper is manufactured from wood pulp and/or cotton waste. China clay or starch is added to paper to give a better writing surface and to make the paper more opaque. Other substances are added to make it water resistant. Paper mills need to be carefully designed and monitored as the process can result in quite heavy pollution of the local rivers e.g. unused fibres, bleaching agents etc.

Paper chromatography A way of separating a mixture of substances in solution that uses paper as the stationary phase.

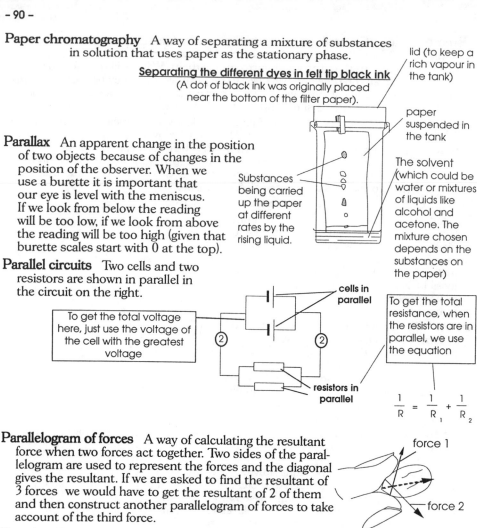

Separating the different dyes in felt tip black ink
(A dot of black ink was originally placed near the bottom of the filter paper).

lid (to keep a rich vapour in the tank)

paper suspended in the tank

Parallax An apparent change in the position of two objects because of changes in the position of the observer. When we use a burette it is important that our eye is level with the meniscus. If we look from below the reading will be too low, if we look from above the reading will be too high (given that burette scales start with 0 at the top).

Substances being carried up the paper at different rates by the rising liquid.

The solvent (which could be water or mixtures of liquids like alcohol and acetone. The mixture chosen depends on the substances on the paper)

Parallel circuits Two cells and two resistors are shown in parallel in the circuit on the right.

cells in parallel

To get the total voltage here, just use the voltage of the cell with the greatest voltage

resistors in parallel

To get the total resistance, when the resistors are in parallel, we use the equation

$$\frac{1}{R} = \frac{1}{R_1} + \frac{1}{R_2}$$

Parallelogram of forces A way of calculating the resultant force when two forces act together. Two sides of the parallelogram are used to represent the forces and the diagonal gives the resultant. If we are asked to find the resultant of 3 forces we would have to get the resultant of 2 of them and then construct another parallelogram of forces to take account of the third force.

force 1

force 2

Parasite Parasites are special kinds of predator. They live in, or on other organisms (their host) and obtain their nourishment at the latter's expense. We don't normally think of caterpillars or aphids as parasites even though they relate to their host plant in much the same way that fleas or mosquitoes do.

force 1

resultant force

force 2

Obligate parasites cannot survive away from their host.
Facultative parasites may be able to survive away from their host.
Partial parasites e.g. mistletoe, are plants which photo synthesise but also parasitise their host.
Ectoparasites live on the outside of the body e.g. fleas, lice, ticks.
Endoparasites live inside their host e.g. tape worms, liver flukes, malaria parasites.

Parenchyma Tissue made of living cells which have large vacuoles filled with gas. The pith in the middle of sunflower stems is a good example of this type of tissue.

Parsec A unit of distance used in astronomy. It is equal to 3·26 light years.

Pascal This is the S I unit for **pressure**. 1 pascal is the pressure when a force of 1 newton acts evenly over an area of $1m^2$. It is a very small unit, 1 atmosphere = 101 325 Pa (Symbol: Pa).

Pasteurisation A process used to kill most of the bacteria in fresh milk. It involves warming the milk to $62°$ C and keeping it at that temperature for 30 minutes followed by rapid cooling. This kills the bacteria without altering the flavour. The modern way is to keep it at $72°C$ for 15 seconds followed by rapid cooling.

Pectins Substances in fruits that are responsible for the setting of jams. Pectins belong to a group of long–chain polysaccharides. They produce jellies because the chains get tangled together forming a network in which the liquid is trapped.

Pectoral girdle In humans it is the set of bones that includes shoulder blades, shoulder joint and collar bone. In other vertebrates it is the bone or cartilaginous structure that supports the fore limbs or front fins.

Pelagic Of the open water i.e. free swimming or drifting creatures or floating plants in lakes or oceans.

Pelvic girdle Skeletal part for attachment of hind limbs or fins in vertebrates.

Pencil lead Now made from graphite mixed with clay. The amount of clay decides how hard the pencil will be. Very little clay means the pencil will be soft.

Penicillin An antibiotic produced by the Penicillium mold. It prevents the growth of several species of bacteria by interfering with their ability to synthesise cell walls. As we don't have cell walls penicillin has hardly any side effects for most humans. We can use it to treat bacterial infections.

Penumbra Half-shadow. It is used when referring to the dimmed light during an eclipse of the sun in regions away from the full eclipse.

Pepsin An enzyme, released into the stomach, that is a powerful digester of protein. It only works in an acid medium.Pepsin acts by splitting the protein into smaller pieces. It is an endopeptidase. There are also proteases that remove amino acids from the ends of the chain (exopeptidases).

Peptide bond The bond that holds amino acids together in proteins. It forms between the carboxyl group and the amine group. A molecule of water is released i.e. it is a condensation reaction. (see amino acid)

Percentage A ratio in which the denominator is 100

$$e.g. \ \frac{1}{5} = 20\% \ \left(= \frac{20}{100} \right)$$

Perennial Plants that continue their growth from year to year (as opposed to annuals which grow from seed into mature plants with flowers all in one season).

Two amino acids joined by a peptide bond
(water will be given off when this bond forms)

amine group

the peptide bond

the water

carboxyl group

Perfect gas A gas in which the particles behave as if they have no volume and where there are **no attractions between them**. Such a gas could be cooled to absolute zero without liquifying and would obey Boyle's and Charles' law throughout the full temperature range. Gases like neon and argon (noble gases) are the closest we have to the theoretical perfect gas.

Period In science it means a cycle which is part of a repeating event. Hence periodic waves, menstrual period, periodic table.

Periodic table When the elements are placed in order of increasing atomic mass a pattern emerges. It is possible to rearrange the list in the form of a table so that elements with similar properties fall into groups. These groups can be quite large e.g. the group of metals or non-metals.

The groups can also be quite small e.g. the alkali metals or the noble gases. Take care to distinguish between period and group.
Period: A row e.g. lithium, beryllium, boron, carbon, nitrogen, oxygen, fluorine, and neon all form one period.
Group: These are arranged vertically, you should be able to list the alkali metals (Group 1), the halogens (Group 7) and the noble gases (Group 0).

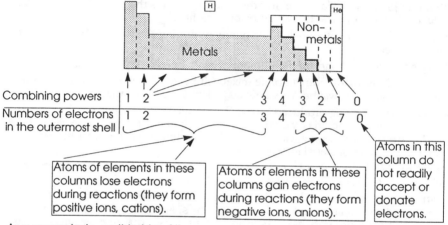

Combining powers   1   2   3   4   3   2   1   0

Numbers of electrons in the outermost shell   1   2   3   4   5   6   7   0

Atoms of elements in these columns lose electrons during reactions (they form positive ions, cations).

Atoms of elements in these columns gain electrons during reactions (they form negative ions, anions).

Atoms in this column do not readily accept or donate electrons.

As a general rule, on this side of the table, elements become more reactive as you move down a group i.e. sodium is more reactive than lithium.

The most reactive element is found at the top of group vii. (with other groups it is variable e.g. N_2 is relatively unreactive)

Peritoneum The lining of the space in which the intestine is found. The outer walls, the gut itself and membranes attaching the gut to the back wall are all peritoneum. This has a very large surface area and so is sometimes used as an exchange surface in medicine. Substances are injected into the space knowing that they will be taken up by the blood. By filling the space with warm plasma substitute (saline solution with added glucose etc.) unwanted molecules will diffuse out of the blood.

Permanent hardness Hardness in water that cannot be removed by boiling. It is caused by calcium and magnesium sulphate but can be removed by adding sodium carbonate.

Permanent magnet A magnet which will not readily lose its magnetism. Until the early years of this century, magnets were made of hard carbon steel. (iron containing 1 to 1.5% carbon). It was then found that the addition of small quantities of tungsten, chromium or cobalt, greatly improved the magnetic properties of the steel. Alcomax, Alnico and Ticonal contain iron, nickel, cobalt and aluminium and are very useful alloys.

Pest control   Five methods for controlling pests are available: pesticides, biological control, altering the agricultural practice to make the area less favourable to the pest, breeding plants for pest resistance and breeding, sterilising and then releasing large numbers of the pest (this only works well with organisms known to mate only once).

Pesticide   Substance used to control agricultural or other pests e.g. insecticides and fungicides. Many of the substances used in the past have now been shown to be quite damaging to humans (e.g. phosphate based sheep dips) or to the environment (e.g. DDT and mercury based seed dressing). This has made a section of the public very uneasy about the methods being used to produce their foods.

Petri dish   Laboratory glassware in the form of a flattened dish with a lid.

Petrol   A mixture composed mainly of hexane, heptane and octane (hydrocarbons with the formulae : C_6H_{14}, C_7H_{16}, $CH_3(CH_2)_6CH_3$). Other ingredients are added to make sure the vapour does not explode too soon during the compression stroke. e.g lead tetraethyl (this is often not added now e.g. 'green' petrol).

pH   This gives us an idea of the acidity of a solution. The pH number is a way of presenting the hydrogen ion concentration $[H^+]$. Here is a way to calculate the pH of a solution when you know the molarity of the H^+.

$$pH = -\log [H^+]$$

1. Enter the H^+ concentration in your calculator.
2. Press the log button (not the ln button).
3. Press the change sign button.
4. The answer in the window is the pH of the solution.
In doing this you have made the assumption that all the H in the acid has dissociated.

Phagocyte   Cells which are able to engulf small particles or bacteria from their surroundings e.g. mast cells wander about the mucosal surface of the lungs ingesting bacteria etc. In the liver, the Kupffer cells ingest damaged red blood cells.

Pharmacology   The study of substances with medical importance found in nature and the effect of drugs and medicines.

Phase   A term used in connection with vibrations or cyclic events. Two waves are said to be in phase when their crests coincide as well as all other parts of the two waves. They are out of phase when crest coincides with trough (or does not exactly coincide with any other crest) (see also change of phase).
Also phase: as in colloids or two or more substances separated by a boundary.

Phenol   Carbolic acid. Very important in the chemical industry. It is a corrosive and dangerous solid which can cause a very severe skin reaction (burns). (C_6H_5OH)

Phenotype   The total appearance of an organism. Phenotype includes the biochemistry of the organism, it is not only about the external appearance.
Phenotype results from the interaction of the genes and the environment.

Phloem   The main food–conducting tissue in plants. Phloem is a mixed tissue containing different types of cells. It conducts glucose and other food molecules away from the leaves and around the plant.

Phosphate   A salt of phosphoric acid, H_3PO_4.

Photochemical smog   Hydrocarbons from car exhausts and nitrogen oxides can react together in the presence of UV to produce an unpleasant smog. These smogs are a particular problem in regions where there is plenty of sunlight and the geography causes air to be trapped so that exhaust fumes build up.

Photoelectric effect   Some substances will release electrons when light of certain frequencies shines on them. Sodium, potassium, caesium and rubidium emit electrons when struck by visible light in the far blue part of the spectrum.

Photon The smallest 'bit' of electromagnetic radiation (.i.e. X-rays, light, radio waves etc.). Photons have zero mass when at rest.

Photosynthesis All life on earth depends on photosynthesis ('All', if we ignore the small group of organisms that live around ocean-bed volcanic vents). Plants use sunlight, carbon dioxide and water to make complex organic molecules and oxygen.

This equation is often used to describe what happens during photosynthsis	$\longrightarrow$	$6CO_2 + 6H_2O \xrightarrow[\text{chlorophyll}]{\text{light energy}} C_6H_{12}O_6 + 6O_2$

The process takes place in the **chloroplasts** when energy from light is used to make molecules of ATP . This **ATP** is then used to help make organic molecules from carbon dioxide and water. ATP (adenosine triphosphate) is a small molecule that readily transfers energy. It is fair to describe it as the fuel for living creatures (but it is recycled much more rapidly than any other fuel). The energy is used to work muscles and power biochemical reactions.

Phylum The larger groups used in the Linnaean system. All animals with an exoskeleton and with jointed legs belong to the phylum Arthropoda. Our own phylum is the Chordata (creatures with a rigid support for the body, usually in the form of a backbone).

Pico– A million millionth i.e. 10^{-12} (Symbol: p)

Pitch of notes The quality of a sound that allows us to place it on a musical scale. The pitch is decided by its frequency e.g. middle C has a frequency of 256 Hz. Notes of different pitch stimulate different parts of the cochlea (see ear for more detail).

Pituitary A small gland (in humans it is the size of a pea) on the lower surface of the brain, located in the middle between the ears. It releases many hormones e.g growth hormone, thyroid regulating hormone, the hormones that control the egg production, antidiuretic hormone and others.

Placenta The exchange organ between mother and embryo in the higher mammals i.e. mammals other than marsupials. The embryo absorbs sugars, amino acids, fatty acids, vitamins etc. from the maternal blood supply. At the same time it is producing carbon dioxide, urea and other substances that must be removed. These are passed out to the mother's blood. The membranes lining the blood vessels in the placenta use energy to move small molecules actively across from one blood system to the other.

uterus wall

the embryo

the umbilical chord

amniotic membrane
(this is part of the embryo's tissue)

the placenta
(afterbirth)

amniotic fluid
(This is 'the water' of 'Oh God ! my waters have broken')

mother's blood vessels

embryo's blood vessels

Planet There are nine major planets. Planets revolve around the sun and other stars and are seen by reflected light, see 'solar system'. The universe has enough stars of the right type for there to be several million planets very similar to Earth orbiting them. There is, therefore, a good chance that life exists elsewhere.

Plankton Very small organisms (plant and animal) living in the upper regions of oceans, lakes and rivers. They are at the mercy of currents as they have little or no ability to move quickly, but many of them migrate to greater depths during the day, returning to the surface at nights.

Plant growth substances (formerly growth hormones) Substances produced at shoot tips and other parts of plants that bring about cell elongation and other effects, and so are involved in plants growing towards the light and roots growing downwards.

Plasma The clear fluid part of the blood of vertebrates, 54% by volume. It clots readily and contain salts, sugars and soluble proteins.

Plasmid A piece of DNA found in bacteria and yeasts. It is not part of the organisms main collection of genes but sometimes carries genes which may prove useful to it e.g. genes giving antibiotic resistance.

Plasmolysis This happens in plants with rigid cell walls. During plasmolysis water leaves the cytoplasm for the outside so that the cell membrane pulls away from the cell wall. The effect can be observed by viewing rhubarb cells in salty water.

Plate tectonics See continental drift.

Platelet (thrombocytes) Produced in vertebrate bone marrow, these little cell fragments are carried in the blood stream. They clump together at the site of any damage to blood vessels helping to block the wound. They also cause the blood clot to constrict, drawing the edges of the wound together.

Pleural cavity The places in which the lungs occur in mammals. There is very little space between the outside of the lungs and inside of the rib cage. The lungs can slide against the outer surface because a fluid lubricates the two layers. This space can become infected with bacteria. If the bacteria cause the lubricating fluid to dry up, the patient suffers pain and gets help. If the fluid does not dry up the patient is often unaware of the condition, feels awful but doesn't really know why.

Plutonium An element with two protons more than uranium. There are 13 different isotopes of plutonium some of which are able to release large amounts of energy and so are used in nuclear weapons. The main energy source in the fast breeder reactor is plutonium.One of its isotopes has a half-life of 24 400 years. (Symbol Pu At.No. 94)

Pole The place to where the magnetic field lines converge.

Pollen Spores of flowering plants. After landing on the female flower, pollen grains germinate and send out a pollen tube. This grows towards the ovary. One of the nuclei in the growing tip of the tube fertilises an ovum. Do remember that a pollen grain is not the equivalent of an animal sperm.

Polar co-ordinates A way of locating a point in space. They consist of a distance from some reference point and the angle made by the object, reference point and some agreed reference line. The polar co-ordinates here are (3·15cm, 33°) (See also cartesian co-ordinates).

Position of the origin 3·15 units Position of the point 33° O

Pollution A huge subject, particularly nowadays. Pollution is a poisonous or harmful contamination of the biosphere. We need to know something about acid rain, air pollution, agricultural pollution, noise pollution, industrial effluent, domestic waste and nuclear waste. We also need to accept (and do something constructive about it) that the people of the developed world produce more pollution than anyone else.

Polygenes Many characteristics e.g. skin colour in humans are not controlled by a single dominant or recessive allele occurring at one locus but by alleles at several loci. These alleles, operating from many loci, are referred to as polygenes.

Polymer A very large molecule made by joining together many (thousands) of smaller molecules e.g. nylon, polypropylene, terylene, 'Dacron' , cellulose, starch etc.

Polymerisation The process of joining molecules together to form long chains. It takes place e.g. when starch is formed from glucose, or when proteins are synthesised in the cytoplasm from amino acids using a molecule of m RNA as the instruction code.

Polymorphism Taking different (many) forms.
   In genetics the term is used to suggest   1. that the different forms are controlled
by genes and   2. that each form, in its own way, is conferring some advantage on
the organism that carries it. e.g. the human blood groups and sickle cell anaemia.

Polypeptide Many amino acids joined together by peptide bonds. All proteins are
polypeptides but not all polypeptides are proteins. Many of the larger proteins are
made of several polypeptide chains. Polypeptides are formed by condensation
reactions.

Polysaccharide Many sugars joined together. Starch and glycogen are polysaccharides as are the fibres in insect cuticle (chitin) or fibres that make up cotton or plant
cell walls (cellulose). Polysaccharides are formed by condensation reactions.

Polythene A polymer made from ethene molecules (ethene: C_2H_4). A tough, waxy,
flexible material that is resistant to acids and alkalis.

Population genetics This studies how the total of all the genes in the population
(the gene pool) have been affected or are being affected. The balance of all the genes
in the population will be changing while evolution is taking place.

Population pyramids These tell us about the age structure of a population. They
are prepared by dividing the population into age groups, then dividing the age
groups into male and female and then presenting these An ideal age pyramid for a
as block graphs back to back. Population pyramids developed society in which most
allow us to predict the rate of growth of populations of the people survive to old age.
and to anticipate the needs of the changing population
with regards to numbers of schools, hospitals, etc..

This example does not show the
sort of blips that occur because
of wars, epidemic etc.

age groups

Males   Females

Numbers of people in each
age group

Portal system In vertebrates it is normal for blood
vessels from the heart to split up into a capillary bed,
the capillaries then come together to form veins which
carry the blood back to the heart. In a portal system
one capillary bed is followed by another before the
blood is returned to the heart. The vessels draining
the gut in mammals then passes into the liver where
the blood passes through another capillary bed.
Gut and liver are supplied with blood in series.

Position effect Many genes will produce a different effect on
phenotype when they are moved from one position in the chromosome to another.
The change is not produced by a mutation that affects the DNA but just by a
change in position. Position effects play an important part in evolution.

Positive feedback This provides a way of bringing events to a final solution e.g.
thinking about food when you are hungry only makes you hungrier and so more
determined to find food. A better example is provided during birth. The contractions
of the uterus push the babies head against the cervix. This stretches the cervix and
this causes a hormone to be released which encourages stronger contractions . . so
more stretching, therefore more hormone, even stronger contractions and so on. The
only way out of this loop is the birth of the baby. (see also negative feedback).

Potential difference This gives us an idea of how much work can be done when
charge moves from one place to another (by any route). As it is an amount of work
done per charge moved we expect joules and coulombs to be part of the units.
   Symbol: V Units: joules per coulomb ($J C^{-1}$)

Pound Imperial unit of mass. 1 pound = $0 \cdot 454$ kg .

Power 1. The rate at which work is being done, i.e. the rate at which energy is transferred.

$$P = \frac{\text{energy transferred}}{\text{time taken}}$$

P = Current x Voltage (P = I V)   Symbol: P.   Units: watts (joules per sec.).

2. Power of a lens or curved mirror is given by $P = \dfrac{1}{\text{focal length (in metres)}}$ (Units: dioptres)

3. A way of indicating that a number is to be multiplied by itself a certain number of times. $8 \times 8 \times 8 = 8^3$ — the power or index — the base

Precipitate An insoluble substance that appears in a solution. Precipitates can form because the solution cools and so some of the dissolved matter comes out of solution. They can also form because dissolved substances have reacted to give an insoluble product. We use the (s) to indicate solid.

e.g. 1 $Ba(OH)_2$ (aq) + $H_2(SO)_4$ (aq) = $Ba(SO)_4$ (s) + H_2O(l)

Precipitation Rain, hail, snow or drizzle etc. . Also 'formation of a precipitate' as in chemical reaction.

Precursor A substance from which another is formed in the course of a chemical process. There are enzyme systems for changing the ammonia to urea. When talking about these reactions we can say that ammonia is a precursor of urea.

Predator Any organism (usually an animal) that gains most (or all) of its nutrition by eating animals.

Pressure $p = \dfrac{\text{Force}}{\text{area}}$ — This force is produced when the particles are bouncing — area of the surface on which the particles are bouncing

Symbol: p.

Unit: pascals (newton per metre^2)

Pressure is not just a force. It is force spread over an area.

other units used include millibars, mm. of mercury and atmospheres.

Pressurised water reactor See nuclear reactor.

Prey An animal that is hunted and killed by a carnivorous animal.

Primary colours Simply stated these are three coloured lights that produce white light when mixed in equal proportions. Red, green and blue lights are primary. When we are dealing with pigments the final colour is arrived at in a different way (a subtractive process) and here cyan, magenta and yellow are the three primary pigment colours. Black is produced when these three are added together in equal proportions.

Prime number A natural number (counting number) that is only divisible by itself and by 1.   e.g. 2, 3, 5, 7, 11, 13 . . .

Printed circuit An electronic circuit that can be fairly easily mass produced. An insulating board is coated with copper and, using a photographic method, the parts of copper that will form the wire are protected with a film. The rest of the copper is then etched away so that just the wires remain. All the components (resistors, transistors, capacitors etc.) can then be soldered into place.

Prism A solid which has two identical faces parallel to each other. These faces are polygons. The other faces are all parallelograms. When a beam of white light is shone through a triangular prism the white light can be seen to split into the colours of the rainbow with red being bent the least and blue the most. When spectra are made with diffraction gratings it is the red light which is bent the most.

Product The result you get when two numbers are multiplied together. $7 \times 5 = 35$

factors product

Product feedback A form of control for biochemical reactions. The product may reduce the effectiveness of the enzymes involved and so the reaction slows down until some of the product is used up whereupon the enzymes become active again. See also negative and positive feedback.

Progesterone A steroid sex hormone produced by the ovaries (and by the placenta during pregnancy). It affects the inner lining of the uterus and other tissue preparing them for implantation. A fall in the blood levels in women initiates menstruation.

Prokaryote Organisms in which the genetic material is not surrounded by membranes. Bacteria and blue–green algae are in this group. (see also Eukaryotes). The ribosomes are smaller than those in eukaryotes. They do not have true mitochondria or chloroplasts.

A diagram showing the main features of a bacterium

flagellum
cytoplasm
granule
slime layer
membrane
nucleoid (no membrane around it)
cell wall
0.5 to 1.5μ m

Proof (of spirits) Brandy and other spirits are said to be proof when their ethanol content is 57·10% by volume. This is the lowest concentration at which gunpowder can be ignited even though wet with spirits i.e. it gave a simple test that the customs and excise inspectors could use when checking whether the public were being cheated. 70% proof means 70% of 57·10% = 39·97% alcohol by volume.

Proper fraction A fraction in which the numerator is smaller than the denominator.

Proportional When we plot a graph of a proportional relationship the line is straight and passes through the origin.

Proportionality constant This is best explained by means of an example:
I want to buy blank cassettes (90 minute). I know that the total cost will be proportional to the number of cassettes I buy (up to a point*) and can write this as:
Total cost α number of cassettes.
The number of cassettes and the total cost are variables and we can set one equal to the other by using a proportionality constant:

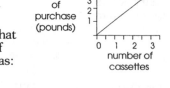

A proportional relationship

total cost of purchase (pounds)

number of cassettes

The proportionality constant, in this case is the price of a cassette

Total cost = constant x no. of cassettes

Prosthetic group A non-protein group which must be attached to an enzyme for the enzyme to work.

* they may give me a discount for a large order)

Protease An enzyme that digests protein. This is usually done by hydrolysing the peptide bond (see also peptide bond).

Protein Substances that are made from amino acids, joined together in long chains. They contain carbon, hydrogen, nitrogen, oxygen and sometimes, sulphur. Proteins may contain up to several thousand amino acids. Proteins show great variety in their structures and properties:

Type of protein	Examples
contractile	muscle protein
strong and inelastic	tendons (composed mainly of the protein collagen)
strong and elastic	ligaments and skin (yellow elastic fibres)
water- and bacteria-proof	skin, feathers, nails etc. (keratin)
catalysts	enzymes
transport chemicals	haemoglobin, serum albumin (transports fats in the blood)
storage	egg albumin
protective	antibodies
toxic	snake venoms
hormones	insulin

Protein sequence (usually referred to as amino acid sequence) The order in which the amino acids occur in a protein. This order is referred to as the proteins primary structure. The secondary structure of a protein is the spiral or other nature of the chain. This spiral occurs because of the nature of the peptide bond. The tertiary structure of the protein refers to the way that the protein chain crumples upon itself to give each protein its own shape. This crumpling is very important in enzymes as it ensures that the active site has the right shape.

Protein synthesis Most of the genes are in the nucleus but proteins are made in the cytoplasm, and so a mobile copy must carry the information (recipe) from nucleus to cytoplasm. This is done by messenger RNA.

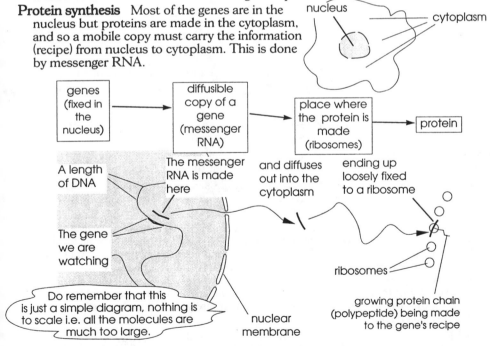

Protista A term which was used for the group of unicellular organisms but now is used for a larger group that includes protozoa, algae and slime fungi.

Protozoa A phylum or sub-kingdom that holds the unicellular and colonial organisms. Amoebae, chlamydomonas, paramecium as well as the malaria and sleeping sickness parasites belong in this group.

Pulsars Astronomical objects that emit pulses of radio waves. The pulse frequency ranges from $0 \cdot 03\,$s to 4 s. They are believed to be star remnants made mainly of neutrons. The pulsing occurs because they spin rapidly (very rapidly for such massive objects).

PVC Polyvinyl chloride. A polymer used for flooring, electrical coverings, clothing, furnishing, packaging, toys and luggage. P VC gives off acidic hydrogen chloride when it burns and so should not be disposed of in this way.

Pyramids These pyramids are diagrams which use boxes to represent the groups of organisms (trophic levels) that act as channels for the energy from the sun. The energy comes ultimately from the sun and, eventually, it is all radiated back out to space. There are three main kinds of population pyramid:

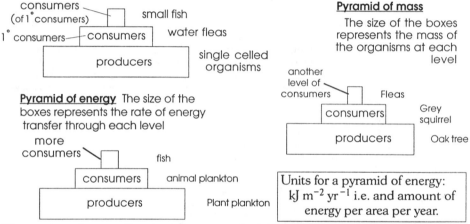

Pyramid of numbers

consumers (of 1° consumers) — small fish

1° consumers — consumers — water fleas

producers — single celled organisms

Pyramid of mass
The size of the boxes represents the mass of the organisms at each level

another level of consumers — Fleas

consumers — Grey squirrel

producers — Oak tree

Pyramid of energy The size of the boxes represents the rate of energy transfer through each level

more consumers — fish

consumers — animal plankton

producers — Plant plankton

Units for a pyramid of energy: $kJ\ m^{-2}\ yr^{-1}$ i.e. and amount of energy per area per year.

Pyrex A trade name for a heat-resistant glass. Pyrex has a high SiO_2 content with some boron and aluminium. It is also known as borosilicate glass.

Pyrogallol ($C_6H_6O_3$) A type of phenol which, in alkaline solution, rapidly absorbs oxygen. As more and more oxygen is absorbed it turns darker brown.

Quadrat This is an area of vegetation, usually chosen by throwing a frame (the frame is also called a quadrat) of set size. These provide us with a valuable way of sampling the vegetation in an area.

Quantum theory A theory that had to be produced when it was found that Newtonian mechanics could not explain many events at the sub-atomic level. Taking a specific example; we know that electrons move away from the nucleus when an atom is heated. Quantum theory suggests that the distance from the nucleus does not increase steadily but that electrons hold one position for a while and then jump to a new position. Electrons with higher energy are unstable and fall back to lower energy levels. Photons of light are given off each time an electron falls back.

Quartile A set of scores can be divided into four equal parts. Each part is a quartile. The median divides the results into a lower and an upper half (see interquartile).

third quartile — 100 / 75

second quartile (also median) — 50

first quartile — 25 / 0

Quartz clock A crystal of quartz can be made to oscillate at about 100 000 Hz. These vibrations are then scaled down and used to work a clock operating in hours, minutes and seconds. Such clocks are accurate to within 0·001 second per day.

Quasar Radio sources which seem to be on the very edges of our universe.

Quenching 1. Inhibiting an electrical discharge. A geiger tube contains a quenching agent which ensures that each spark is quickly damped out. This allows the tube to measure radiations arriving very close together.
    2. Rapid cooling of metal by dipping it in oil or water. It causes hardening of steels but softening of non–ferrous metals like copper.

Questionnaire A series of questions, designed to establish the attitudes of people to some chosen subject. The tricky bit about questionnaires is to get the questions right. The questions must not lead to (prompt) certain answers in favour of others.

RAD A unit for the absorbed dose of radiation. It gives an idea of how much energy has been released in tissue. 1 RAD = 0·001J per kg of irradiated material

RAM (the symbol for relative atomic mass is Ar) Relative because it is the atomic mass of atoms when compared to the mass of a carbon 12 atom, taken as being 12 units. (RAM is not an official abbreviation)

ROM Read Only Memory.

Radar (radio detection and ranging) A system that sends out pulses of microwaves and collects the reflections. The time between sending the pulse and receiving the reflection, as well as the strength of the reflection, give position and size of the object.

Radial symmetry Any diameter drawn across the shape will split it into two halves that are mirror images of each other. Sea urchins, jelly fish and many flowers show radial symmetry.

Radian A radian is the angle at the centre subtended by an arc of one radius. It is the SI unit of plane angle. 1 radian = 57·296° Symbol: rad

Radiation Any form of energy that travels as rays, waves or streams of particles. Most commonly, the term is applied to light and other electromagnetic waves, sound waves and the emissions from radioactive substances.

Radiation sickness Ionising radiation (such as is given off by radioactive materials) can damage cells and genes. The level of sickness produced by radiation depends on the dose received. The **brain** is amongst the least susceptible organs and so if the dose is large enough to damage brain cells, the victim will die within a few hours. People who receive a smaller dose will die in a few days because of damage to the **intestine**. People who receive an even smaller dose can die in a few weeks because of damage to the blood-producing system. In the long term, people who survive the initial radiation have an increased chance of suffering from various cancers and they may produce abnormal children. Symptoms include fever, nausea, vomiting and diarrhoea. Later there can be shedding of skin and hair.

Radical The root of a plant embryo i.e while it is in the seed or during germination.

Radio carbon dating By comparing the proportions of ^{14}C in the dead organism with the levels of ^{14}C in living tissue today, the age of the dead material can be calculated. The date depends on the assumption the the levels of ^{14}C have not changed over the last 10000 years. ^{14}C is constantly being produced in the atmosphere due to the effect of radiation from the sun on ^{12}C. It is then incorporated into plants which are eaten by animals.

Radio frequencies Frequencies in the range 3 kHz to 300 gigahertz (GHz).

Radioactive series Atoms which give off radiation will change to an atom of another element. Often the element produced is also radioactive and decays further. Uranium (^{235}U) decays eventually to lead. The elements that appear as decay continues form part of a series. In the case of ^{235}U

$$^{235}_{92}U \xrightarrow{\alpha} {}^{231}_{90}Th \xrightarrow{\beta} {}^{231}_{91}Pa \xrightarrow{\alpha} {}^{227}_{89}Ac \xrightarrow{\beta} {}^{227}_{90}Th \xrightarrow{\alpha} {}^{223}_{88}Ra \xrightarrow{\alpha} {}^{219}_{86}Rn \xrightarrow{\alpha} {}^{215}_{84}Po$$

$$^{207}_{82}Pb \xleftarrow{\beta} {}^{207}_{81}Tl \xleftarrow{\alpha} {}^{211}_{83}Bi \xleftarrow{\beta} {}^{211}_{82}Pb \xleftarrow{\alpha}$$

Radioactive tracing Using radioactivity to see what is happening during chemical reactions. People were able to answer some questions about photosynthesis by supplying plants with radioactive CO_2 for brief periods, and then finding out what simple carbon substances contained the radioactivity.

Radioactivity The spontaneous disintegration of the nuclei of atoms of certain elements with the emission of **alpha** or **beta particles**, sometimes accompanied by **gamma rays**. When an alpha particle is given off, the nucleus loses 2 protons and so a new element is formed (the new element is two places back on the periodic table) When a beta particle is given off, a neutron has changed to a proton and an electron. The nucleus has gained a proton, forming a new element (the new element is one place higher on the periodic table).

Radon A noble gas (atomic number 86). Its most stable isotope has a half–life of 3·825 days. With such a short half–life we wouldn't expect there to be any left so long after the big bang, but there is because it is produced due to the radioactive decay of radium. With improved insulation of housing, radon can build up inside to dangerous proportions.

Random Totally due to chance i.e. every member of the set has an equal chance of being chosen.

Random sample Whenever we collect results we try to be as **objective** (see page 3) as we can. If we are trying to measure the dandelion population of a field, it is wrong to hunt out those parts of the field that have clusters of dandelions on them. We use a number of techniques to ensure that our samples are completely random (quadrats, line transects, belt transects, etc.).

Range The absolute difference between the largest and the smallest measure. When several readings are taken of the same event they should all be close together. The range often gives us an idea of how well things went (see also standard deviation).

Rate A comparison of one quantity with another e.g:
     speed of car: 21 metres per second (ms^{-1})
     rate of reaction: this can be given as the rate of disappearance
     of reactance or as the rate of appearance of product molecules,
     rate of exchange of Greek and UK currencies: 135 drachmas to the pound.

Ratio A comparison of two or more quantities (or the fraction the first quantity is of the second). Two stroke fuel for the mower may be 25 petrol to 1 of two stroke oil. This is abbreviated to 25 : 1 (this is a rich mixture).

Reaction Before they can react, particles have to bump into each other and the collision must be a hard one (hard enough to bring about bond breaking). Chemical reactions involve the outer electrons of atoms. Energy is always transferred and new compounds are produced during a reaction. During reactions, electrons change their position (see ionic and co–valent bonds).

Reaction rate Only a small fraction of the collisions which take place between the reactants are violent enough to bring about a reaction. To speed up reactions, we must increase this fraction, make sure that lots of the particles have the necessary activation energy.

Speeding up the reaction rate can be done in the 6 ways shown on the next page.

1. Make the reactants more concentrated.
2. Grind up the solids so that they have a bigger surface area.
3. Raise the temperature.
4. Use a catalyst (for the best results use the catalyst with the largest surface area. Negative catalysts slow reactions down).
5. Shake the reactants more vigorously.
6. Squash gases by increasing the pressure on them.

Real images An image that can be cast on a screen.

Recessive Alleles which are completely recessive will only show their effect when the organism has two of them i.e. when the organism is homozygous for that allele. Many alleles which we think of as being completely recessive, do express themselves slightly even though there is only one recessive allele e.g. the sickle cell allele has a slight effect on erythrocytes when only one is present.

Recessive lethal Alleles which are rare in a population but which carry information for some life threatening characteristic. We all have these and so should not have children by close relatives (who have a good chance of carrying the same lethals).

Reciprocal quantity 1 divided by the quantity i.e. $\frac{1}{quantity}$ e.g the unit of conductance (the mho) is the reciprocal of the unit of resistance (the ohm).

Rectifying (ac to dc) Changing alternating current to direct current (see diode and full wave rectification for one method used).

Rectum The final section of the alimentary tract. Faeces are stored here for a while.

Recycling The recovery and re-use of materials from wastes. It has been going on ever since life began as natural recycling . Natural recycling can be summarised in the carbon, nitrogen, sulphur, water and phosphorus cycles.
As the human plunder of the world's natural resources continues, recycling becomes increasingly important.
Recycling falls into 3 classes: 1. re-use e.g. milk bottles.
                                  2. direct recycling. Items which are directly recycled at the site of production because they fail to meet certain standards. Offcuts can also be recycled in this way.
                                  3. indirect recycling. This involves the collection of materials after use, followed by sorting cleaning and reprocessing. We are only just beginning to reach the stage where the possibility of recycling is taken into account at the design stage so that materials are easily separated at the end of the life of the object.

Red blood cells Erythrocytes. See blood cells.

Red giants Stars which are believed to have been like our sun but, having lost about 10% of their mass, have enlarged and cooled down slightly and so appear red (see stellar evolution).

Redox Oxidation-reduction reactions. These don't need to involve oxygen. We now consider redox reactions as being ones in which electrons move from one atom, molecule or ion to another. The particle which loses electrons is said to be oxidised, the particle which gains electrons is said to be reduced.

Red shift A change in colour towards the red end of the spectrum (doppler shift). It is of great importance in astronomy. A star, moving away from us, would appear redder than we might expect. The more the light has shifted the faster the star must be moving away. Our universe seems to be expanding. Stars furthest from us seem to be moving away fastest (have the greatest red shift) (see also doppler effect and Hubble's constant).

Red tide Change in the appearance of the sea due to a population explosion of unicellular organisms. These are often quite toxic, causing death of fish etc.

Reducing sugar A sugar that is able to act as a reducing agent i.e. it can donate electrons. Glucose and some other monosaccharides are reducing sugars. Sucrose is not.

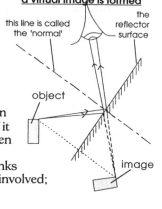

A diagram showing how a virtual image is formed

Reflection Both waves and particles are reflected from surfaces in a predictable way. Reflection takes place at the surface that separates two different media. In this case, air and the metal of the silvered surface at the back of the mirror.

As a general rule: Angle of incidence = angle of reflection

Reflex A response that doesn't require us to be aware of it e.g taking the hand away from fire. These reflexes happen very quickly because the nerve signals do not need to pass to the brain first. The signal travels to the spine, links with other fibres and travels straight out to the muscle involved; no thinking is needed at first.

Reflex angle An angle between 180° and 360°.

Reflux condenser Apparatus which recycles the volatile components in a mixture by boiling and recondensing. It can also be used to boil a solution for a long time without loss of vapour.

Refraction Waves change direction when they change their speed e.g. light rays bend as they pass through a prism. Sound will refract as it passes from cold air to warm air (this forms part of the explanation as to why sound travels so well over water). No bending will occur if the rays arrive at right angle to the reflecting surface (i.e. along the normal).

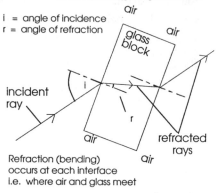

A diagram showing a ray of light passing through a glass block

i = angle of incidence
r = angle of refraction

Refraction (bending) occurs at each interface i.e. where air and glass meet

Refractory Materials that are not damaged when they are heated to high temperatures e.g. fire bricks, asbestos.

Relative atomic mass The ratio of the average mass of an element to $1/12$ of the mass of ^{12}C. By giving the common isotope of carbon an atomic mass of 12, we can use it as a standard and work out the atomic masses of all the other elements.

Relative density A ratio that compares the density of a substance with that of water (used to be known as specific gravity). For mercury it is 13·6, for oak, 0·80.

Relative humidity The ratio of the amount of water vapour in the air with the amount of water vapour that the air could hold if it were saturated. Many creatures cool themselves by evaporating water from their skins. This takes place rapidly when the relative humidity is low (evaporation occurs quite slowly when the vapour content is low but the air is cold i.e. the relative humidity is high).

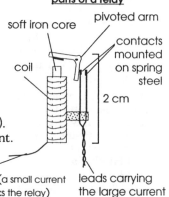

A diagram showing the main parts of a relay

soft iron core
pivoted arm
contacts mounted on spring steel
coil
2 cm

Relay The diagram on the right shows one arrangement. When the small current flows the soft iron core becomes magnetised and pulls down the pivot arm which forces the contacts together.

control leads (a small current along these works the relay)

leads carrying the large current

Renewable energy (Alternative energy) These are energy sources that do not rely on fossil fuels or nuclear fuel. Renewable energy sources include: hydroelectric power, biofuel (e.g. willow coppice for power stations, sugar alcohol for cars), solar energy, tidal energy, wind energy, and wave energy.

Replication The process by which 'things' make copies of themselves. The breeding of animals and plants provide examples of replication as does the manufacture of the new genetic material (DNA) from existing DNA.

Reproduction The process by which organisms make copies of themselves.
Vegetative reproduction produces new organisms that are genetically identical to the parent e.g. strawberry plants can reproduce by sending out runners.
Sexual reproduction involves mixing of genetic material from two parents. The offspring are genetically different. These differences provide variation so that species can change as the environment changes.

Repulsion A separating force like the one felt when the north poles of two magnets are pushed together.

Resistance Electrical resistance gives us an idea of how hard it is for electrons to flow along a conductor. We have a formula for calculating the resistance of a component: The resistance of a material depends largely on the number of free electrons that there are around the atoms. The more there are, the lower will be the resistance. See 'parallel' for details of calculating resistance in circuits.

Symbol : R   Units : ohm $(J \, s \, C^{-2})$ $R = \dfrac{V}{I}$ — Voltage (Joules per Coulomb)

— Current (Coulombs per second)

Resistor A piece of electrical apparatus with a known resistance. Carbon resistors are widely used. One kind are made from finely ground carbon, mixed with a ceramic material. This is then packed into a small tube and painted with colour- coded rings. Wirewound (coils of wire; usually manganin) resistors are also used.

Resolving power The ability of a microscope or telescope to let us see two objects as separate even when they are very close together. This will depend on the wavelength used as well as on the quality of the lenses. The shorter wavelengths allow greater resolving power.

Two objects, close together, showing their appearance when viewed with different microscopes.

O O objects

good   poor
resolution resolution

Respiration. 1. Internal respiration. During this process energy is released from substances like glucose or fatty acids. It happens in the cytoplasm of cells, both in the cytoplasm sap and in the mitochondria. Enzymes are essential to this process. During **aerobic respiration**, chemicals (usually carbohydrates or fats) are oxidised to give carbon dioxide, water and energy (in the form of Adenosine triphosphate, ATP).

Glucose + Oxygen $\longrightarrow$ Carbon dioxide + Water + energy

$$C_6H_{12}O_6 + O_2 \longrightarrow 6CO_2 + 6H_2O + \text{energy (in the form of ATP)}$$

During anaerobic respiration the energy is released without using oxygen. In animals, lactic acid is an end product of this kind of respiration. In plants, the end product is alcohol. In most organisms, anaerobic respiration is only a short term solution to energy needs when oxygen is in short supply, because both alcohol and lactic acid will damage tissue as their concentrations rise.

$C_6H_{12}O_6 \longrightarrow 2CO_2 + 2C_2H_5OH + \text{Energy}$
Glucose $\longrightarrow$ Carbon dioxide + Alcohol + Energy

$C_6H_{12}O_6 \longrightarrow 2CH_3CHOHCOOH$
Glucose $\longrightarrow$ Lactic acid $\longrightarrow$ Carbon dioxide + Water
+ Energy   + Energy

this step happens when oxygen becomes available again

Respiration 2. External respiration. Breathing or ventilation

Respiratory quotient This is a ratio, i.e. carbon dioxide produced : oxygen consumed during aerobic respiration. Molecules containing oxygen (e.g. carbohydrates) will use less oxygen than molecules which have little oxygen (e.g. fats). Some respiratory quotients: Carbohydrate is 1, Fat is 0·7, Protein is 0·8. Measuring the respiratory quotient of organisms can give us an idea of their main source of energy.

Resultant The resultant of two forces is the force that will have the same effect. We can calculate the resultant by drawing a parallelogram of forces. If we add two or more **vector** quantities together we will always get a resultant (see parallelogram of forces).

Retina Surface at the back of the eye that contains cells that are sensitive to light (rods and cones). The rods and cones connect with neurones so that when light strikes one of them a nerve impulse will travel to the brain. The neurones connect together in a way that improves the resolving power of the system (see also rod).

Retrograde motion This is shown by the planets. If we follow them as they move, day by day, against the background of the stars, they seem to travel in one direction for a while, then slow down and start to travel back on themselves. They then stop and speed up again on their original course. The effect is an illusion that results from the fact that we observe the planets from a moving earth.

the arrow-heads mark the planet's position after equal time intervals

Retrovirus Viruses that carry their genetic information on RNA but which transfer the information to the host's DNA after infecting cells. Once this has happened it becomes very difficult to treat the condition. The HIV virus is of this type.

Reverse osmosis Using high pressure to squeeze water from brine. The method is used to get drinking water in desert areas with access to the sea. Pressures of up to 25 atmospheres are used to push the water through a semi–permeable membrane. The method cannot be used on a large scale because of the high pressures needed.

Reversible reactions These are reactions which can go in either direction. e.g. H_2O can break down to give H^+ and OH^-. But H^+ and OH^- can also join together to form water.
We use two arrows ($\rightleftharpoons$) to show that the reaction is reversible.

$$H_2O \rightleftharpoons H^+ + OH^-$$

Rheostat A variable resistor (electrical).

Rhesus factor Some people (and certain monkeys) have a particular protein on their red blood cells. Such people are said to be Rh^+. People without this protein (Rh^-) will produce antibodies to it if they receive Rh^+ blood. This is only really a problem for Rh^- mothers whose partner is Rh^+. As the Rh^+ gene is dominant the developing baby may be Rh^+. Small amounts of this blood leak onto the mother's side of the placenta and stimulate antibody production. The first child is often unaffected but further babies can have their red blood cells destroyed by the rising levels of antibody (making them anaemic). Fortunately the medics have now found ways of reducing the chances of damage to the babies.

Rhizome Underground stem that grows horizontally such as is found in mint and couch grass. They allow vegetative reproduction to occur.

Ribosomes Tiny granules of RNA and protein. They can be free in the cytoplasm or bound to membranes (the **endoplasmic reticulum**). Proteins are synthesised on ribosomes. Ribosomes also occur inside mitochondria and chloroplasts (see also protein synthesis).

ribosomes bound to E.R.

Richter scale A way of grading the intensity of an earthquake. The scale is so arranged that each whole number increment indicates a ten fold increase in the energy levels (i.e. it is a log scale, like the pH scale). Buildings are damaged at values greater than 6 on the Richter scale.

Ringer's solution A salt solution designed to be gentle on living tissue and cells. The solution is buffered so that it resists changes in pH. It contains the salts normally found in tissues i.e. sodium, potassium and calcium chlorides. Recipes for more sophisticated physiological solutions are now available. These take account of the special needs of different tissues e.g. insect wing muscle or other.

RMS value (See root mean square)

RNA (ribonucleic acid) Single stranded or looped molecule which are composed of bases and sugar phosphates. The sugar in the backbone is ribose rather than deoxyribose (as found in DNA). There are three types of RNA: messenger, transfer and ribosomal. (See also protein synthesis and DNA).

Rock cycle In its strictest sense 'cycle' refers to a sequence of events which returns to its starting point. In the rock cycle the sequence needs to start with weathering and erosion.

Rock cycle

Weathering — Erosion — Transportation — Deposition — Subsidence — Metamorphosis — Uplift

Rod A cell that contains pigments that react to light. When light is absorbed by the pigment a nerve impulse is produced. Rods are affected by light of any wave length. They are found in the retina of vertebrates and the higher molluscs e.g. the squid.

Retinal rod cell

pigment

light

Root The part of a plant that usually holds it in the soil, and absorbs minerals and water from the soil. True roots should contain elongated vessels that conduct water with dissolved minerals to the rest of the plant.

Root cap Loosely arranged cells covering the end of growing roots. The cap protects the root from damage as it is forced through the soil by elongating cells a bit further back in the root.

Root hair Hair-like outgrowths from epidermal cells on roots. These grow out between grains of soil and humus and so are vital in absorbing minerals and water from the soil.

Root Mean Square This gives a way of working out an average. It is particularly useful when we need to get an average value for A.C. voltage or sound intensity. If all we did was to add all the values and find the average we would get zero for the answer because half the values are positive and half are negative. Instead we find the RMS value. We square all the values (that removes any negative signs), add them together and calculate the mean and then find the square root. See alternating current for more details on peak values and RMS values.

Roughage The fibrous indigestible part of our food that passes, almost unchanged, through our gut. Roughage does a lot more than just stimulate healthy muscular action in the intestine. Roughage particles have a large surface area and could have a very important role in absorbing nasty chemicals, like nitrosamines, onto their surface. This would keep these chemicals out of the body and so reduce the chances of them triggering cancers.

Rounding Before we can round up decimals we need to know how accurate the answer is. We then look at the next figure, if it is less than 5 we can ignore it. If it is 5 or more we increase the previous figure by 1.

4·772918 becomes 4·77   to 2 decimal places (d.p.)
or   4·773 to 3 d.p.   (see significant figures)

Ruminants Herbivores with the first part of their intestine (the stomach) modified to allow bacterial fermentation of their chewed food. Most herbivores have a real problem in that their food is quite bulky and difficult to digest, and so having special bacteria increases the nutrients that can be released from the molecules. Ruminants include cattle, sheep, goats, deer, antelopes and giraffes.

Rust An oxide of iron.For rusting to occur there must be moisture and air in contact with the iron.

Saccharide A simple sugar e.g. glucose, fructose (both are $C_6H_{12}O_6$, i.e. both have the same molecular formula)

Saccharin ($C_6H_4SO_2CONH$) A substance with about 550 times the sweetness of sucrose but without any food value.

Saline Usually the term refers to salt solutions used when studying cells or tissues. The saline is made up so that it is as close to the normal fluids found surrounding cells or tissues. The pH is buffered i.e. kept close to a chosen value (see also Ringer's).

Saliva Fluid secretion from glands in the head of arthropods and vertebrates. It can contain enzymes (starch digesting amylases) and mucus. In blood sucking organisms (mosquitoes, vampire bats etc.), the saliva contains anticoagulants so that the blood keeps flowing freely. The saliva of many mammals contains substances with antibacterial activity.

Salt Salts are made by reacting an acid (e.g. acetic acid or hydrochloric acid) with a metal (e.g. sodium or calcium) or base (e.g. calcium oxide, zinc hydroxide). Salts are ionic and all the salts that you are likely to meet will have a metal part (the positively charged cation) and a non-metal part (the negatively–charged anion).

$$CuO + H_2SO_4 = CuSO_4 + H_2O$$

Metal part. (Copper ion)

Non-metal part. (Sulphate ion)

The salt

Salt bridge A way of keeping two solutions in electrical contact but prevented from mixing e.g. a tube of potassium chloride in gel.

Salting out A way of precipitating one dissolved substance from a solution by increasing the concentration of another (the second is usually a salt). As an example, a soap in solution can be precipitated out by adding table salt. It also gives us a gentle way of separating proteins out from a solution.

Sand Generally this is composed of small granules of impure silica (SiO_2). Sands are produced from rock disintegration.

Saturated compound A compound which does not contain double (or multiple) bonds between the atoms. Hard fats are also described as saturated fats. Oils with many double bonds in the molecules are called polyunsaturated.

Saturated solution A solution that cannot hold any more solute. Strictly it is a solution existing in equilibrium with excess solute (as solids). If you raise the temperature of most saturated solutions they will no longer be saturated.

Sawtooth graph Such shapes can be produced by electrical circuits such as multivibrators. Voltage rises steadily and then falls steadily but more steeply. The shape shown is ideal, usually the sharp points are rounded.

A sawtooth graph

Voltage

Time

Scalar A quantity which has only size (i.e. magnitude). Mass, volume, speed, height, distance and depth are all scalar quantities (Vectors have both size and direction).

Scanning Electron microscope A microscope that uses a focussed beam of electrons bounced off the specimen. The reflections are treated electronically to give a very detailed picture of the surface. The resolution is very good with details of a hundred millionth of a metre being clearly visible (10^{-8}m).

Scintillation Flash of light. Usually the term is used for such flashes when they are produced by radiation (ionising radiation). A scintillation counter contains a substance which gives off a flash of light when struck by ionising radiation (e.g. zinc sulphide for alpha particles). Because everything happens very quickly it is necessary to count thousands of events per second.

Sedimentary rock Rocks formed from sediments. Most sedimentary rocks are formed under the sea. They show strata (layers). There are three categories.
1. Rocks that are derived from fragments of existing igneous, metamorphic or sedimentary rocks that have been eroded, transported and deposited by wind or water. These are known as **clastic** rocks and they can be classified according to sediment size. Coarse sediments; breccias and conglomerates. Finer sediments; sandstones. Fine sediments; shales.
2. Organic sedimentary rocks which are formed from the remains of animals and plants e.g. limestone and chalk from the remains of sea creatures, coal, oil etc.
3. Chemical sedimentary rocks which are formed from the precipitation of minerals, usually by evaporation, from both sea and fresh water. Some limestones and flints are formed in this way.

Seed A plant embryo with a supply of nutrients (starch, fats, oils, protein etc) surrounded by a protective coat. The embryo will not begin growing until water and warmth are available. As a general rule, seeds are virus free.

Seeding Adding fine particles to a solution to produce crystallisation. Seeding is also used as a way of getting clouds to drop their rain. Finely ground silver salts are dropped into suitable clouds.

Seismograph An instrument for measuring earth tremors. The tremors begin in places where one lot of rocks grate against another. There are seismograph stations all around the world collecting results 24 hours a day (see also earthquake).

Selective breeding Traditionally most breeding programmes in agriculture involve breeding only from those organisms that possess the qualities that we want e.g. short stalks in barley plants, good milk production in cows. Genetic engineering (in which we insert the particular genes we want) is playing a large part now in programmes aimed at improving agricultural stocks.

Selfish gene A concept. The idea is very simple and like so many brilliant ideas, is pretty obvious once someone has thought of it. Organisms are programmed so that almost everything they do is done to increase the chances that it will be their genes that are passed on to the next generation. At its simplest level it explains why the dominant lion seeks out and kills any young cubs the moment they take over a new pride. It might also explain why aunts and uncles feel closer to their blood nephews and nieces than they do to their spouses nephews and nieces.

Semiconductor A conductor whose resistance decreases as the temperature rises. This is because, as the temperature rises, more and more electrons are knocked free from their atoms. These electrons can drift if a voltage exists across the crystal, giving **N-type conductivity**. **P-type conductivity** occurs because of the positively charged holes (the holes are left when the electrons are knocked free) in the crystal.
Continued on the next page.

Semiconductor (continued) Semiconductors can be made from elements or compounds e.g. Germanium, silicon, selenium and lead telluride. Transistors and other electronic components are made from semiconductors. They have revolutionised electronics because they need so little current for them to work, because they can be made so small i.e. circuits using them are compact and economical because they don't wear out.

Semipermeable membrane A membrane with many minute holes in it (the holes are molecular in size). The holes will only allow some dissolved particles to diffuse through. Particles that are too large (or that carry the wrong charge) will be trapped on one side. Such membranes are also known as differentially permeable (see also dialysis).

Series circuit. Electrical components that are arranged one after another in such a way that electricity has to flow through each one in turn. We get the total resistance (or voltage) by adding the values of the separate resistors (or cells).

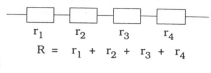

$$R = r_1 + r_2 + r_3 + r_4$$

Sex A process that allows genetic material from two different individuals to mix. This is important for any species as it provides variation within the population.

Sex chromosomes Chromosomes that determine the gender of the offspring. In humans, chromosomes (labelled X chromosomes) have been shown to be present in both female and male. The shorter Y chromosome is normally only found in males. Having two Xs in every cell makes an individual female. An XY combination in every cell results in a male.

STD Sexually transmitted diseases. The self-referral STD clinic at your local hospital is often referred to as the GUM clinic (gynocological urinary medicine).

SHC See specific heat capacity.

S I units (Système International d'Unités). This is the internationally agreed system of units for use in science and elsewhere, in which the metre, kilogram and second form the basic units.
There are a number of conventions that we are asked to conform to:
1. Capitals are not used for symbols unless the unit is named after someone thus: newton has the symbol N but metre has the symbol m . capitals are never used for the full name of a unit e.g. watt, hertz etc.
2. there is no space between the m and m of millimetre i.e. mm (e.g. km, ms, etc.)
3. There is a space between combinations of derived and basic units e.g. N m
4 the letter 's' in never used to indicate the plural. 100 millimetres is written '100mm'
5 When writing numbers with S.I. units the digits are arranged in groups of three, and a space is placed between each group.(hence 557 832.54cm). A number with only 4 digits is written without spaces.

Shock wave Moving regions of **compression** and rarefaction (longitudinal waves) that spread out from some sudden event e.g. an explosion or an earthquake. Shock waves also spread out from the front edge (leading edge) of an object moving through a fluid at speeds greater than the speed of sound. Shock waves transfer energy (as do all waves).

Sickle cell anaemia A genetic condition (found in parts of west Africa) in which the red blood cells appear crumpled whenever oxygen is in short supply. It is controlled by the sickle cell allele and is fatal for individuals possessing two such alleles (i.e. individuals who are homozygous for the condition). It has not died out in these populations because individuals with only one allele per cell (heterozygous for the condition) have greater resistance to malaria than normal individuals.

Sidereal time If we judge day length by the stars, we get one time (sidereal day length), if we judge it by the sun we get another (the solar day). The period of rotation of the earth on its axis with respect to the fixed stars. A sidereal day is slightly shorter than our solar day by 4·09 minutes (see day length for a diagram).

Sievert This is a measure of the biological effect of radiation.
Number of sieverts = the dose in grays x Q
(where Q is a quality factor i.e. how dangerous the radiation is).
The sievert is the SI unit of dose.

Sigma (Σ) Used to indicate that all the numbers in a set are to be added together.
Thus: Σ (marks of each candidate) asks us to add up all the class marks.

Signal to noise ratio This gives us an idea of how much useful signal is getting through. (e.g. music versus atmospherics)

Significant figures Rounding 376 628 to:
  1 significant figure gives 400 000
  2 significant figures gives 380 000
  4 significant figures gives 376 600

Rounding 0·00063728 to:
1 significant figure gives 0·0006
2 significant figures gives 0·00064
7 significant figures gives 0·0006373

(See also rounding)

Silica Silicon dioxide a hard white solid which is the main ingredient of sand.

Silicon The element with atomic number 14 (RAM 28). It is in the same group as carbon and so has similar chemical properties.

Silk Fibrous protein produced by spiders and certain insects. The silk used to make cloth comes from the silk moth fed on mulberry leaves. It is very useful in fashion because of the textures possible and because it takes up colours very strongly.

Sink A term used in science to indicate some system that is able to absorb large amounts of a substance, energy, sound etc. We might say that the liver is a sink for glucose because, given certain conditions, it seems to absorb so much of the glucose that appears in the bloodstream.

Sinus A space. This may be filled with blood, air or some other substance. Humans have large air–filled sinuses behind the nostrils, eyebrows and in the cheek bones.

Skin Outer covering of many organisms. The diagram below shows the main features of animal skin.

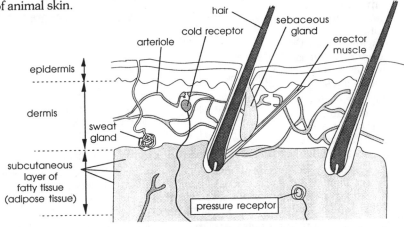

Slag The non–metal substances that end up floating on the molten iron during the smelting process.

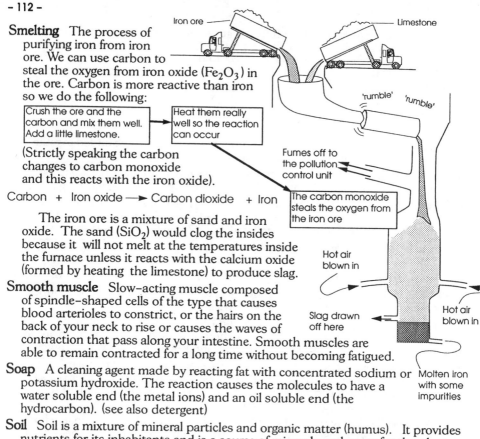

Smelting The process of purifying iron from iron ore. We can use carbon to steal the oxygen from iron oxide (Fe_2O_3) in the ore. Carbon is more reactive than iron so we do the following:

| Crush the ore and the carbon and mix them well. Add a little limestone. | → | Heat them really well so the reaction can occur |

(Strictly speaking the carbon changes to carbon monoxide and this reacts with the iron oxide).

Carbon + Iron oxide ⟶ Carbon dioxide + Iron

The iron ore is a mixture of sand and iron oxide. The sand (SiO_2) would clog the insides because it will not melt at the temperatures inside the furnace unless it reacts with the calcium oxide (formed by heating the limestone) to produce slag.

Smooth muscle Slow-acting muscle composed of spindle-shaped cells of the type that causes blood arterioles to constrict, or the hairs on the back of your neck to rise or causes the waves of contraction that pass along your intestine. Smooth muscles are able to remain contracted for a long time without becoming fatigued.

Soap A cleaning agent made by reacting fat with concentrated sodium or potassium hydroxide. The reaction causes the molecules to have a water soluble end (the metal ions) and an oil soluble end (the hydrocarbon). (see also detergent)

Soil Soil is a mixture of mineral particles and organic matter (humus). It provides nutrients for its inhabitants and is a source of minerals and water for the plant roots that penetrate it. Plants get their energy from the sun. From the soil, they remove elements like sodium, potassium, magnesium and copper as well as nitrates and phosphates.

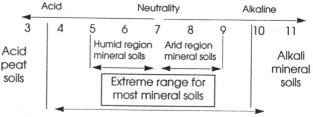

Most British soils have pH values between 5 and 7.

Solar flares Bursts of hot material that shoot out from the sun into space. Solar flare activity affects radio communications on Earth.

Solar system The system of nine planets and the belt of asteroids, revolving in almost circular orbits around the sun. The orbits are very nearly circular and lie very nearly in the same plane (The planets in order are : Mercury, Venus, Earth, Mars, Jupiter, Saturn, Uranus, Neptune and Pluto).

Solar wind Charged particles stream out from the sun all the time but the intensity varies over the months and years. It is composed mainly of protons and electrons. This stream sweeps past Earth, distorting our magnetic field, causing radio interference and the aurora borealis amongst other effects.

Solenoid   Usually a uniform coil of wire which is long in comparison to its diameter. Solenoids are a central part of many remote control switches. Allowing a current to flow in the coil will result in a magnetic field which can be used to move the switch mechanism (see relay for a diagram that shows one possible arrangement).

Solution   In a solution, each particle of the dissolved substance (the solute) is completely surrounded by solvent particles. This means that the solute particles are kept separated and so will not settle out of solution.
The important characteristics are that solutions are the same throughout (homogeneous) and there is no tendency for the solute to precipitate.
It is possible to have solutions of solids in solids (e.g. alloys) , gas in solids, liquid in solids as well as solids in liquids and liquids in liquids. (but most examples of these last four are regarded as colloids) Concentration is usually given in grammes of solute per 100g solvent or grammes of solute per 100g solution.

Solvent   A substance (usually a liquid) which can dissolve other substances.

Somatic   Of the body. Somatic cells are all cells of an organism other than gametes i.e. ova, pollen nuclei or sperm.

Sound   Those 'shock waves' , transmitted through the air, that can cause a response in the healthy ear. Sound spreads as longitudinal waves and is caused by a vibrating object e.g. the diaphragm of a loud speaker.
High notes have shorter wave lengths than low notes.
The energy level of the sound needs to increase by about 26% for the ear to detect a change. This amount of increase is known as a decibel (dB). The ear is more sensitive to some frequencies than to others so that some sound may seem louder than other sound even though the intensity, measured in watts per square metre is the same for both sounds.   Velocity of sound ≈ 330 m s^{-1} (in air). The S.I. unit for sound intensity is 'watt per square metre' , measured at right angles to the line of travel of the sound.

Specific thermal capacity   The specific heat capacity of a substance is the amount of energy that is needed to raise the temperature of 1 kg of the substance by 1 K.
Units: joules per kilograme kelvin

$$\text{S.H.C.} = \frac{\text{Energy transferred}}{\text{mass x change in temperature}}$$

Species   Members of the same species are phenotypically similar and can breed successfully with each other to produce fertile offspring. In some cases it can be difficult to decide on the boundaries between two separate species as the organisms may look identical and yet keep to distinct breeding populations.

Spectrum   A range of wavelengths presented in an orderly array e.g. the colours of the rainbow. The term is not only applied to visible light.

Speed   The rate at which something moves.
Speed is given by the gradient of a distance/time graph

$$\text{speed} = \frac{\text{distance}}{\text{time}}$$

Units: metres per second m s^{-1} (derived units)

Speed–time graph

Sphincter   A ring of smooth muscle surrounding a tube. The sphincter muscles can relax , allowing material to pass, or close, sealing off the tube. There are sphincters at either end of the stomach: the cardiac and pyloric sphincters.

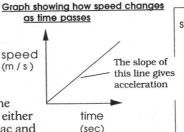

Graph showing how speed changes as time passes

speed (m / s)

The slope of this line gives acceleration

time (sec)

$$\text{slope} = \frac{\text{rise}}{\text{run}}$$
$$= \frac{\text{speed}}{\text{time}}$$
$$= \frac{\text{m s}^{-1}}{\text{s}}$$
$$= \text{acceleration}$$
Units: m s^{-2}

Spinal cord The nerve cell bodies, nerve fibres and support cells that pass along the back of vertebrates. The cord is protected by the vertebrae. Sets of paired nerves leave it at each vertebra. It carries sensory and motor information which include signals that control involuntary reflexes. A hollow space down the centre is filled with cerebro-spinal fluid.

Spore These are reproductive structures. They are usually very small and given off in large numbers by some green plants, fungi, bacteria and protozoans. One type of spore serves to spread the distribution of the organism. They are produced in vast numbers and spread by wind or water. Spores are also used by organisms that need to get past a difficult period.

Stable Not likely to break down. As in 'stable isotope' which is an isotope that will not disintegrate and give off radiation.

Standard deviation Standard deviation gives us a fairly straight forward way of comparing the spread of our results. E.g. we could measure the length of 100 mature acorns and then calculate the mean length. Our results would cluster around this mean spreading out on either side of it. The method set out in a to e below shows how to calculate the standard deviation.

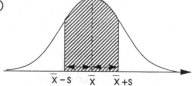

mean

spread of acorn lengths

The graph below shows what part of a normal population fits within one standard deviation on either side of the mean.

a) find the mean $(\bar{x})$
b) find the deviation of each variable (x) from the mean $(x - \bar{x})$
c) square each deviation and add them together $\Sigma(x - \bar{x})^2$
d) divide the total by the number of variables (n)
e) take the square root of your answer.

Standard deviation (s) $= \sqrt{\dfrac{\Sigma(x - \bar{x})^2}{n}}$

$\bar{x} - s$ $\bar{x}$ $\bar{x} + s$

About 68% of the area of the curve lies within one standard deviation of the mean.

Standard index form This gives us a convenient way of writing very large or very small numbers. The idea is to rewrite the number as a number between 1 and 10 multiplied by another number (a power of 10) which will put the decimal point in the right place.
289 000 000 becomes $2\cdot89 \times 10^8$ or   0·000 000 000 375 6 becomes $3\cdot756 \times 10^{-10}$

Star A twinkling object in the night sky. The light that we see has set out from an object very much like our sun i.e. a huge object in which hydrogen is being changed to helium in a controlled way releasing vast amounts of energy (most stars are controlled hydrogen bombs).
Gravity will tend to make the star very small but this is prevented from happening because the steady stream of radiation that moves outwards from within the star. The star's size is therefore a balance between inward force due to gravity and an outward force due to the stream of radiation moving out through the star.

Starch Many glucose units linked together in a branched structure.

Static electricity A concentration of electrons which are not able to move somewhere else at the moment. (e.g. electrons on the surface of a non–conductor or on the dome of a Van de Graaff generator). If static is allowed to build up it can sometimes cause fires when the electrons finally move as a spark. This happens in flour mills or other places where the air can become filled with dust which will burn.

Statistics Don't be put off by all those jokes about lies, damned lies and statistics. Statistics can be misused but they are also hugely useful in helping us make decisions when the answer is not clear cut. Statistics involves collecting data and describing it in a way that makes it easy to understand e.g. displaying as a table, a diagram or graph. It then becomes much easier to see the trends.

Stellar evolution Current theory holds that stars begin when gas collects together due to gravitation. The gravity forces get larger as more matter is added and will eventually cause such strong compression at the centre of the matter (mainly hydrogen) that a nuclear reaction begins. Hydrogen is converted to helium and huge amounts of energy are given out. This state lasts for several billion years. The forces due to gravity are causing the star to collapse but it is prevented from doing so by the stream of energy and particles moving away from the centre. The next stage is a gradual enlargement to form a red giant and then as more and more matter is lost from the star it collapses to form a white dwarf. The main sequence of events is set out in the Hertzprung–Russell diagram.

Sterile Free from micro–organisms or unable to produce gametes that can take part in a fertilisation.

Steroids A group of alcohols (sometimes considered to be lipids because of their high carbon–hydrogen content). Many occur naturally in animals, acting as hormones. Testosterone, oestrogen, progesterone as well as cortisone and many other all belong to this group.

Stomata See guard cell (page 62).

Strain The movement caused by a force (stressing your ankle badly often causes a strain). It is the ratio of change compared to the original measurement.

Strata Layers such as are found in sedimentary rocks. A stratum is one layer.

Streptomycin An antibiotic which acts against many bacteria but does have disadvantages; it can affect the nerves supplying the ears.

Stress In physics it is a force applied to some object (see strain). In everyday usage it means those pressures that now seem to be a part of daily life. Some people find it helpful to divide stress into **positive stress**: pressure that we can handle. We know exams are near but we have worked steadily and done well so far so that we feel we can handle it. **Negative stress** on the other hand is pressure on us to perform in way that we can't possibly manage; we have got into debt and are falling behind with the mortgage, then we lose our job. We are now being expected to do the impossible.

Striated muscle See muscle.

Strong acid If we say that hydrochloric acid is a strong acid we do not mean that it is very concentrated. The term strong means that it forms ions very readily. If is does this then there will be many H^+ and so the acidity will be high.
Strong: releases many H^+ ions. Concentrated: there is much of it in solution.

Sublime To change straight from solid to gas without passing through a liquid phase. Dry ice (solid CO_2), and aluminium chloride.

Substrate The substrate is the molecule on which an enzyme acts when it catalyses the reaction. In such reactions there will be substrates and products.

hydrogen peroxide ⟶ oxygen + water
substrate / the enzyme involved here is catalase / products

Sulphate A salt of sulphuric acid (H_2SO_4).

Sulphide A salt of hydrogen sulphide (H_2S).

Sulphite A salt of sulphurous acid i.e. containing SO_3^{2-}.

Sunspot (eleven year cycle) Large darker patches on the surface of the sun. They increase in number with time reaching a maximum every 11 years. The temperature of the surface in the sunspot is about $4000°C$ less than the surroundings.

Superconductivity The resistance of metal conductors to electricity, decreases as the temperature falls. As the temperature approaches absolute zero (0 K) all electrical resistance should disappear. In practice, for most metals, the flow of current heats up the metal so that it cannot reach 0 K. For some metals and alloys (lead, vanadium, tin) resistance abruptly disappears a few degrees above 0 K. These are superconductors. As resistance is zero, very large currents can flow without a significant heating effect. People get excited about this as it allows them to make the kinds of intense magnets used in the magnetic suspension for trains etc. Initially this work concentrated on temperatures near absolute zero, but now the work is focussing on finding superconducting alloys that work at the temperature of liquid nitrogen (about $-170°C$) (these temperatures are much easier to maintain than temperatures close to absolute zero)

Supernova An exploded star that becomes 100 million (10^8) times brighter than our sun during the process. Only 6 of these have been observed in our galaxy. A supernova is believed to begin because the star runs out of the hydrogen that powers it. It collapses under gravity, spins faster and new nuclear reactions occur in which heavier elements are produced. The energy of this latest reaction causes the star to explode. The matter from which Earth is made could have arisen in this way and been collected by our Sun's gravity.

Surd An irrational number. It cannot be expressed as a fraction or exact number. e.g. π or $\sqrt{2}$ are surds.

Surface area It is largely surface area that decides how rapidly energy or water will be lost from an organism. In fact it is the amount of surface area to each bit of volume (the surface area to volume ratio) that is really important. As organisms get larger their surface area to volume ratio gets smaller and they have increasing difficulty in losing heat.

Suspension Small solid particles suspended in a liquid.

Switch These can be bistable i.e. they will remain in one of two positions. Most light switches in the home are bistables. Switches can also be biased to stay off, like a door bell switch, or biased to stay on, like a fridge light switch (these are monostable). Transistors are switches that can switch on and off very quickly (up to a few million times each second).

Symbiosis A relationship between two different organisms that live together. The term is most often used when one or both organisms get a benefit from the relationship i.e. it is not used for parasitism. Cows and other ruminants have a symbiotic relationship with the fermenting bacteria in their stomachs. The bacteria get benefit from living in a warm place with a regular supply of vegetation. The cows are able to absorb a share of the breakdown products as well as being able to digest any bacteria that travel further down the intestine.

Sympathetic nervous system This controls activities that are normally involuntary like heart rate, intestinal peristalsis or sweating (part of the autonomic nervous system i.e. the sympathetic and parasympathetic systems)

Synapse The junction between one neurone and the next. A nerve signal is triggered on the next neurone because a substance is released and diffuses across the space. Synapses only allow signals to pass in one direction.
Some synapses act as inhibitors and so can control the flow of signals about the system.

Syncline A saucer-shaped fold in folded rock (hollow side upwards).

A diagram showing the main features of a synapse.

vesicles containing transmitter substance

axon

cell body of the next neurone

the synaptic cleft — a 20 nm gap

nanometre i.e. 10^{-9} metres

direction

Systemic A substance that works by entering the body of the organism as opposed to acting by contact with the surface. Systemic weedkillers are absorbed and spread throughout the plant so that even the roots are killed.

T–cells White blood cells that are produced in the bone marrow and settle in the spleen or lymph nodes. There are several types; a type that helps other cells produce antibodies, a second type that release lymphokinins (substances that stimulate other cells to engulf foreign particles), and a type that recognise tumour cells or cells infected by virus and kills them.

Taxis A movement towards something as a result for some stimulation. Taxis involves locomotion and not just growth towards. Plankton may swim towards the light i.e. showing positive phototaxis.

Taxonomy The study of organisms with a view to arranging them in groups. We rely on taxonomists to provide us with a natural classification system for all organisms.

Teflon (polytetrafluoroethene) A very slippery material that can survive temperatures of 400°C. It is used to line non–stick pans, bearings and as electrical insulation.

Telophase The last stage of mitosis or meiosis (see mitosis).

Temperature In very simple terms this is a measure of the average kinetic energy of a particular collection of particles e.g. the particles in a cup of tea. The temperature of a body indicates which direction the energy will flow when that object comes in contact with another object at a different temperature. Unit: kelvin (K).

Tendon A cord-like structure that joins muscle to bone. Tendons are composed mainly of a flexible fibrous protein (closely packed collagen fibres) . Tendons do not stretch very much under load.

Teratogen Substances, radiation or other factors that can cause damage to the embryo.

Terminal velocity The next time that you jump from an aeroplane, notice that whilst at first your body accelerates, it soon reaches a steady speed. This steady speed is reached when the forces dragging you and the Earth towards each other (gravity) are the same size as the force slowing you down (drag). You have reached your terminal velocity. Terminal velocities can be decreased by spreading out your arms, opening your parachute etc.

Territorial behaviour Many animals defend a space from members of their own species. This space is their **territory** and the way that they behave whilst defending it is the territorial behaviour. As a general rule, animals fight less and less fiercely as they move from the centre of their territory. Some animals are only territorial during the breeding season e.g. robins, pheasants and many antelope.

Testosterone A male sex hormone that brings about the development of many male characteristics. Its most obvious effects are to increase aggression and stimulate the development of muscle. It is mainly produced in the testes.

Tetrapod Amphibia, many reptiles, birds and mammals (wings and arms count).

Thermions Any ion emitted by a hot body e.g the filament in a light bulb gives off thermions.

Thermocouple A temperature measuring device made by joining two lengths of wire, each of different metals. One end is kept at a reference temperature (e.g. ice/water mixture). The other joined end is placed at the measuring point. Thermocouples can be made small enough to probe into the skin and so measure skin temperatures during exercise. They work because when two wires are joined like this a voltage is produced if there is a temperature difference between the joints. The voltage increases as the temperature difference increases.

Thermodynamics The study of the laws that govern energy, and energy transfer. Simply stated these are:
First law: Energy is conserved; in a system of constant mass energy can neither be created nor destroyed.
Second law: Energy tends to flow from hot bodies to colder bodies.
Third law: This law concerns entropy at absolute zero but the outcome of it is that absolute zero can never be reached.

Thyroid gland Gland in the neck region of vertebrates. It produces hormones involved in controlling the metabolic rate. Iodine forms an important part of the hormones and if there is too little in the diet the creature will suffer e.g. the condition known as cretinism results when iodine is missing from the diet (this happens to people living in mountainous areas where the steady rain has washed the iodine compounds from the soil).

Tides Movement of the seas because they are being pulled by the gravity of moon and to a lesser extent the sun. The forces involved are pretty staggering. Imagine how much force must be involved in speeding up the whole North Sea so that it travels at about 4 miles per hour in one direction. Six hours later it is moving at 4 miles per hour in the other direction. These kind of movements are going on all around the world. The energy transferred eventually appears as heat and the moon slows down in its orbit around the Earth by a tiny amount each day.

Time Unit: the second (s).

Tissue Groups of cells with a common structure and function. The water–conducting tissue in plants (xylem), the nutrient–conducting tissue in plants (phloem), the oxygen conducting fluid in animals (blood), the contractile tissue of animals (muscle) are all examples of tissues. Organs are composed of groups of tissues, working together e.g. the heart, stomach, leaf, flower, brain, kidney etc.

Tissue culture Growing cells in the laboratory in glass or other containers. The cells must be supplied with all the nutrients they need and kept in conditions that are as like their normal environment as possible. These conditions are ideal for the rapid growth of bacteria, fungi etc., and so the workers need to learn to work under sterile conditions.

The equipment needed for a titration

Titration In our science course we may have used titrations to find out the exact concentration of a particular solution (an acid or alkali). To do this we neutralise a measured volume of the solution in the flask with a neutralising solution of known concentration. A few drops of indicator are added and then the exact volume of solution used from the burette is measured. It is important to work accurately and record all the results. We can then calculate the concentration of the unknown solution.

burette

pipette

Tomography A way of using computers to analyse X-rays that have passed through an object. The X-ray generator rotates around the object. The final result is a detailed picture of one plane of the object. The object (patient) gets about a fifth of the dose used in a normal X-ray.

Tonsil Tissue involved in resisting infection that occurs at the back of the mouth in tetrapods. Some of the white blood cells, produced in bone marrow, are changed into a more active form in tonsils. This also happens in other lymphoid tissue (e.g. the lymph glands in the groin or arm pits).

Toxin Any poisonous substance produced by an organism. Many toxins help the organisms that produce them e.g. poisons in plants and animals like the puffer fish or many toads reduce the number of creatures that can use them for food. Our bodies can make proteins that combine with toxins and neutralise them (certain antibodies do this).

Trace elements These elements are required in minute amounts for healthy growth. For plants these include zinc, boron, manganese, copper and molybdenum. For many animals iodine, copper, manganese, zinc, fluorine, molybdenum and others.

Trait We use this term for a particular phenotypic characteristic e.g. skin colour (controlled by polygenes) or round seeds/wrinkled seeds in peas (controlled by alleles from a single locus). (It is not used in a general way for all possible seed types)

Transect A sampling technique which collects specimens along a line or belt. It is particularly suited for organisms that are fixed in place e.g. vegetation or the small creatures and weeds on a rocky shore.

Transfer RNA (tRNA) These bond with particular amino acids in the cytoplasm. They are part of the mechanism for assembling amino acids in the correct order when polypeptides are made. See protein synthesis.

Transformer Electrical equipment that is able to change voltages of alternating current.

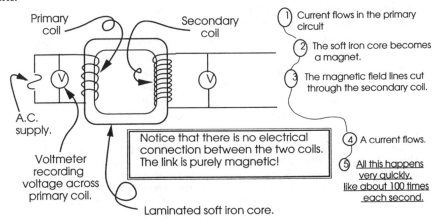

1. Current flows in the primary circuit
2. The soft iron core becomes a magnet.
3. The magnetic field lines cut through the secondary coil.

Notice that there is no electrical connection between the two coils. The link is purely magnetic!

4. A current flows.
5. All this happens very quickly, like about 100 times each second.

Primary coil. Secondary coil. A.C. supply. Voltmeter recording voltage across primary coil. Laminated soft iron core.

Transformers are used to change voltages either up or down. This equation states the pattern:

$$\frac{\text{Number of turns in primary coil}}{\text{Number of turns in secondary coil}} = \frac{\text{Voltage across primary coil}}{\text{Voltage across secondary coil}}$$

This equation gives the voltage 'out':

$$\text{Secondary voltage} = \frac{\text{Number of turns in secondary coil}}{\text{Number of turns in primary coil}} \times \text{Primary voltage}$$

Transistor Transistors are electronic switches. The controlling current is supplied through the **base** lead. This switches on the transistor so that a larger a current flows from the collector to the emitter. Transistors are much faster that electromagnetic switches. Some transistors can switch on and off millions of times each second. Transistors are able to produce a 20 to 100 fold increase in the size of the output current.

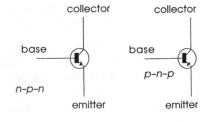

Transpiration   The loss of water vapour from plants into the air. The transpiration stream is the movement of water from soil into roots, up the stem (through xylem vessels) and out to the leaves eventually leaving through the stoma.

Transverse wave   e.g. light waves, waves on the surface of water and some earthquake waves.

Triangle of forces   A way of using a diagram to calculate the force that results when two forces are added together (see parallelogram of forces for a diagram).

Triglyceride   Three fatty acids linked by a glycerol molecule. Animal and vegetable fats are mainly composed of these (see fatty acid for a diagram).

Trilobite   Members of an extinct group of arthropods that can be very common in the fossil record of some areas. Average length of 5 cm.

Tritium   Hydrogen atoms with two neutrons as well as the single proton. It is radioactive (half–life of 12·5 years), atoms fusing to form helium and giving off β radiation.

Trophic level   This is a theoretical term used in ecology. It indicates the steps through which energy passes as it moves along the food web. Each step, grazing, predation, parasitism, decomposition, etc. provides us with a different trophic level. There is a limit to the number of trophic levels that can be found in any food web because energy is lost from the web at each stage. Eventually there is not enough left to pass on. The energy is lost because of movement and heat production. Eventually it all appears as heat. As a very general rule about one tenth to one fifteenth is transferred to the next trophic level.

Trypsin   Protein digesting enzyme produced by the pancreas. It is produced by parts of the pancreas and is released in an inactive form.

Tunnelling   Very very very occasionally chemical reactions can occur which seem to have bypassed the need for activation energy. This is referred to as tunnelling.

Tweeter   A small loudspeaker that is specifically designed to reproduce high frequencies faithfully.

Ultrasound   High frequency sound (above 20 000Hz). This can be used to clean equipment (in water), to check for cracks in metal objects and to study organs.

UV   (wavelength: 4×10^{-7} to 5×10^{-9} metres) Short wavelength electromagnetic radiation just beyond the visible blue region. UV affects photographic plates and is damaging to living matter. It can be used to sterilise equipment and spaces (e.g. operating theatres). Damage to the ozone layer allows more UV to reach the Earth's surface and this will cause problems for plants as well as animals (getting sunburnt is the least of our worries on this score).

Unconformity   A geological term is used to describe that part of a rock profile where there is a major break in the sequence of sedimentation.

A section through some strata showing an unconformity

the unconformity

Universe   All the matter, energy and space that we can experience or guess at. At present we believe that our universe contains about 10^{41} kg of matter collected in 10^9 galaxies. The evidence points increasingly to the chances that our universe has not always existed but that it began fifteen thousand million years ago (15×10^9) as the result of an explosion and has been expanding ever since. The other possibility is that it has always existed (the steady state theory of the universe) (see Hubble's constant and Big bang as well as Dark matter and Galaxy).

Urea ($CO(NH_2)_2$)   An organic compound produced when proteins or amino acids are broken down. It is toxic and so is removed from the body in the urine.

Ureter   The tube that carries urine from the kidney to the bladder in most vertebrates.

Useful work   If a lorry carries a load up a hill the total work done is given by:

Total weight of lorry, driver, fuel and load (in N) x distance raised (in m).

The useful work done is given by: Weight of load only (in N) x distance raised(in m).

Vaccine   A substance used to give immunity from some infective agent like the tuberculosis bacterium or the polio virus. Vaccines are made from whole organisms (which may have been inactivated) or from substances extracted from the infective organisms. They work by stimulating our immune response so that we make antibodies to the particular agent.

Vacuole   A space in the cytoplasm of cells that is surrounded by a membrane and filled with clear fluid. Plant cells tend to have very large vacuoles, animals cell vacuoles are much smaller. Cells of bacteria and blue–green algae do not have vacuoles.

Vacuum   A space in which there are no molecules or atoms. Such perfect vacuums cannot be achieved.

Vagus nerve   A large nerve that carries both motor and sensory information. It originates in the brain and has effects on the heart, intestine and other parts.

Valence   Another word for **combining power** of an atom. It it not much used now.

Valence electron   An outer electron of an atom that is involved in a chemical reaction.

Van der Graaff generator   A device for producing high voltages. Voltages of a million volts can be obtained by making the dome 2 m across.

Van der Waal's forces   Weak attractive forces that occur between atoms or molecules.

Vapour   Molecules of a substance existing as a gas. All solids and liquids give off vapours (e.g. brass has its own particular smell because atoms leave the surface (vapourise) and get into our noses).

Variable   In maths and science these are terms that take a range of values. As an example when we measure the extensions produced by force on a metal spring we are dealing with two variables. The force (which can have a range of values decided by the experimenter, the independent variable) and the extension (whose size depends on the force chosen and the characteristics of the spring used, the dependant variable.

Variation The differences between the individuals in a population i.e. differences in genotype and phenotype. These differences can be of two types:
Continuous variation shows a complete range of types between the two extremes e.g. black hair through all the shades of brown to blond hair. Such variation is usually controlled by **polygenes**. **Discontinuous** characteristics lack intermediates e.g. attached and unattached ear lobes.
Individuals with identical genotypes can still show variations because their environments have not been the same during development.

Vascular bundle Strands of tissue involved in conducting water (as in xylem) or conducting the products of photosynthesis (in phloem) about plants.

Vector Any physical quantity which needs its direction to be stated in order that it be completely described e.g velocity, momentum, force (see also resultant & scalar).

Vein A blood vessel carrying blood from capillaries back to the heart.

Arteries	Capillaries	Veins
Have thick elastic walls	Walls are only one cell thick and the walls contain no fibres.	They have thin but strong walls and are not very elastic.
Have a regular circular shape when seen in cross-section	Are very narrow, often only the width of a red blood cell. Walls are leaky and allow glucose, amino acids and other molecules through.	They appear flattened in cross-section.
Have no valves except in the heart itself		Valves are spaced regularly along their length and act together with nearby skeletal muscles to move the blood back to the heart.
They carry blood away from the heart. Not all arteries carry oxygen rich blood.	They carry blood between arteries and veins	
Blood flows quickly through them and it flows in surges	Blood flows quite slowly and fairly smoothly, there is time enough for the diffusion of substances into and out from the blood.	Blood flows fairly quickly and smoothly.

Velocity Speed in a particular direction. Symbols: u or v (initial or final velocity)
  Units: $m\ s^{-1}$ Useful equation: $v = \dfrac{distance}{time}$, $v = u + at$

Ventilation The process of getting air into and out of the lungs. Mammals have diaphragms as well as muscles between the ribs. The two sets of intercostal muscles move the ribs. The abdomen muscles push air out of the lungs and the diaphragm muscles draw air into them. For gentle breathing the natural elasticity of the lungs is enough to push the air out of them. (see intercostal muscle)
We need to be careful not to use the word respiration when we mean breathing. Respiration is what happens in cells when energy is released by biochemical processes.

Vermiculite Minerals containing mica that expand on heating so that a light granular material is produced. This is a very good insulator and, as it will absorb water, it can be incorporated in cement or concrete to make floor or other insulation (mica: minerals with aluminium, silicon, potassium in them).

Villi Fingerlike projections found on the inside lining of the small intestine

Vinegar A 2 to 4 % solution of ethanoic acid in water (CH_3COOH).

Virtual image A virtual image is one that cannot be cast onto a screen. Our reflection in a mirror is a virtual image. We can see virtual images because our lens focuses the rays onto our retina. No matter how brightly I light my face I will not get a reflected image of it from the mirror onto the bathroom wall.

Virus These are minute infectious agents. They cannot multiply unless they are inside the living cells of their host. They should not really be regarded as alive because they have no enzymes of their own (they can also be crystallised). They trick the cell into making more copies of virus by slotting their own (viral) DNA into the cell's DNA. This is one of the reasons that they are so difficult to treat with medicine; any medicine which damages them is also likely to damage their host cells. Diseases: Poliomyelitis,influenza, measles, mumps, herpes,chickenpox and others.

Viscosity This is a measure of runnyness. Cold golden syrup is quite viscous unlike petrol which has low viscosity. Molten lava of the Hawaiian type also has a relatively low viscosity. Viscosity is measured in pascal seconds ($Nm^{-2}s$). The units make sense once you consider that we are thinking of the liquid as made of layers and measuring the resistance to sliding one layer over the other.

Vitamin These are organic molecules that animals require in small amounts if they are to remain healthy. The animals cannot make vitamins themselves but have to take them in with their diet (we can synthesise Vit. D in our skins but only if we get certain substances in our diet). Vitamins can be divided into two groups:
    water soluble (B-complex vitamins, vitamin C),
    fat soluble (vitamins A, D, E, K).
If we don't get enough vitamins in our diet, we will suffer from a deficiency disease e.g. lack of Vit. C causes scurvy.

Vitreous Glass-like.

Volcano These can be totally nasty or quite friendly depending on the melting point of the magma that 'flows' from them. If the melting point is low (Hawaiian type) then the vent is less likely to become blocked and so pressure does not build up and cause unpleasant bangs and pops, as happened in the Mount Pele or Mount St Helens explosions. If the melting point is high, the magma can solidify in the vent. Pressure builds up and the final explosion is pretty spectacular. Dust can be thrown 20 km into the atmosphere, frightening the life out of the locals but giving the rest of us lovely sunsets for weeks and weeks.

Voltage The amount of energy that the electrons can transfer as they move about the circuit. The voltages around the circuit should always add up to give the same voltage as the supply.

A Coulomb is the amount of charge that is carried by 6.24×10^{18} electrons.

If twenty joules are transferred when this number of electrons passes between two points, then the voltage between the points is 20 V.
Symbol: V Units: Joules per coulomb
                  (abbreviated to Volt)

$$V = \frac{P}{I} \qquad V = IR$$

Voltage divider (potential divider) Resistors in series which can be tapped at different points to give different voltages (see the diagram above).

Voltameter It's important to remember that there is a difference between a voltmeter, which measures voltage, and a voltameter, which is used to measure the quantity of electric charge that has passed through a circuit.

Voltmeter A device used to measure the voltage across some component in a circuit. Voltmeters are **always connected across the component i.e. in parallel** !

- 124 -

Wall (cell wall) Thickened support layer outside the cell membrane of plant cells and bacteria. In plants these are composed of cellulose fibres held together with small amounts of protein or tannin, or pectin. These walls are permeable to dissolved substances; the cell membrane is the barrier to movement in and out of the cytoplasm. Cell walls show huge variation. They can be very thick (as in the gritty stone cells in pears), they can have holes that allow a fluid stream to pass (as in xylem vessels and phloem sieve tubes) or they can be very delicate (as in the pithy parenchyma tissue).

Warfarin A substance that prevents the blood from clotting. It interferes with vitamin K and large doses of vitamin K act as an antidote. It is used as rat poison because it has no taste, little smell, and is slow acting. Rats are very cautious and are also good learners. If one of the rat feels poorly within a few hours of eating something, others in the group will reject that food from then on. This makes finding a suitable poison very tricky which is why rats are such a problem (well . . . that and the fact that people are too casual about throwing away uneaten fast food).

Water cycle Almost all our water has existed as water most of the time since the Earth began. Organisms and rivers have used this water over and over again. A diagram showing the water cycle describes how this happens. It should give details of evaporation from the sea, the formation of clouds leading to precipitation, the return to the sea by rivers, the transpiration from plants, its movement as underground water, its use by animals and its purification by micro-organisms.

Water potential This term is used to refer to the tendency of a system e.g. a cell's cytoplasm, to donate water to its surroundings. The water potential of pure water at one atmosphere is defined as being zero. Any solute added reduces the water potential to a negative value. When osmotic pressure is high, water potential is low. Symbol: ψ_w , water potential = wall pressure + osmotic pressure ($\psi_w = \psi_p + \psi_o$)

> e.g. plant cell wall

Water softener 1. Sodium carbonate or other. This precipitates the calcium or magnesium compounds that are responsible for the hardness. Sodium ions do not cause hardness.
   2. Ion exchange resin loaded with sodium chloride (NaCl). This allows sodium ions to leave the resin and for the calcium and magnesium ions to cling on.

Watt The unit for power i.e a rate of energy transfer equal to a joule per second.

It is a derived SI unit. Symbol: W   Useful equation: $\text{Power} = \dfrac{\text{Energy transfer}}{\text{time taken}}$

Wave length The distance from one crest to the next or from one trough to the next (or from any point on one wave to the equivalent point on the next wave).
Symbol: λ Useful equation: velocity = frequency x λ

Examples of the sizes of certain wavelengths of EMR

The electro-magnetic spectrum	gamma rays	X-rays	ultra violet	visible light	infra red	radio waves
	very short wavelength (i.e. 10^{-13} m)	10^{-8} m to 10^{-12} m	4×10^{-7} to 10^{-8} m	wavelength (blue 4×10^{-7} m red 8×10^{-7} m)		long wavelengths; (i.e. 1500 m)

The sound spectrum as detected by the human ear				the microwaves used in radar fit in here	
	Lowest freq. detectable		middle C		highest detectable freq.
	20 Hz (wavelength = 16.5 m)		256 Hz (wavelength = 1.29 m)		20 000 Hz (wavelength = 0.017 m)

Weak In chemistry this term means that the substance does not release its ions into solution very readily. Hydrochloric acid is a strong acid (it ionises almost completely in water) whereas vinegar (ethanoic acid) is a weak acid since it ionises to form H^+ only slightly. Concentration is something completely different. Concentration tells us how much is dissolved in each volume. It doesn't give any idea as to how many ions are present.

Weather front When a huge mass of warm air pushes against a huge mass of cold air, the place where they join is the front.
Warm front. Mare's tails seen high in the sky usually mean that a warm front is on the way.
Cold front. Where a rolling mass of cold air pushes against a mass of warm air.

Weed A rose bush in a wheat field is a weed i.e. any plant growing in the wrong place (as far as humans are concerned) is a weed.

Weight Your weight is the force that results when gravity acts on your mass (weight is therefore a vector quantity whereas mass is a scalar quantity). Obviously it follows from this that weight depends on gravity. If you are far away from the attraction of other objects, you can be weightless. You will still have a mass though, so a force will still be needed to speed up or slow down your body.

Welding Joining materials (e.g. metals or plastics) by causing them to melt and fuse along the junction. As hot metals tend to react with the oxygen in the air the region of the weld is sometimes surrounded with an inert gas like argon. The argon soon leaves the site of the weld but by that time the temperature has fallen. Welding can be done either using a hot flame (acetylene and oxygen or atomic hydrogen and oxygen) or using an electric arc.

White dwarf A collapsed star nearing the end of its life as an emitter of light. Typically a white dwarf is about the size of Earth but contains about 60% of the mass of our sun. They make up about 10% of our galaxy. Colours range from blue, through white to brown. They will eventually stop emitting light after a billion years or so. Our universe is not yet old enough to have any such dark objects yet.

WIMP Weakly interacting massive particle. Suggested by astronomers to account for some of the missing mass of our universe.

Woofer A loudspeaker specifically designed to reproduce lower audio frequencies accurately.

Work The transfer of energy. We calculate the amount of work done by multiplying force moved, by distance through which it moved i.e. Work = force x distance
Symbol: W   Unit: joules.   Useful equation: $W = F \times d$ (see also useful work)

X-ray Electromagnetic radiation lying between ultra violet and gamma rays in the spectrum. X-rays can be produced by bombarding matter with a high-energy beam of electrons. X-Rays are selectively absorbed by bone and iron-rich tissues (e.g. human blood) and so can be used to get shadow pictures of the inside of the human body. As repeated doses of x-rays can cause cancers, care is needed (see also tomography).

X-ray crystallography When we pass a beam of X-rays through a crystal, the layers in the crystal cause the X-rays to produce a pattern which can be recorded on film (a diffraction pattern). This pattern can be used to confirm our ideas about the arrangement within the crystal.

X-ray tube To make a stream of X-rays we cause a beam of fast moving electrons to crash into a tungsten target. The higher the accelerating voltage the shorter the wavelength.

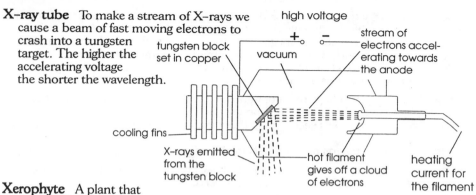

high voltage

stream of electrons accelerating towards the anode

tungsten block set in copper

vacuum

cooling fins

X-rays emitted from the tungsten block

hot filament gives off a cloud of electrons

heating current for the filament

Xerophyte A plant that is suited for life in an environment in which available water is scarce. These would include deserts or salt marshes beside the sea or elsewhere. There is plenty of water in salt marshes but the osmotic pressure is very high and so plants have difficulty in absorbing it.

Xylem Water conducting tissue in plants which also provides mechanical support. Xylem vessels form the bulk of the wood in trees and other woody plants.

Yard British unit of length. 1 yard = 0·9144 metre

Year The time taken by the Earth to complete an orbit of the sun. It is 365·24 mean solar days.

Yeast A common unicellular fungi. Several species of yeast are useful to humans in bread making or in producing alcohol by fermentation.

Yield point This is the point at which atoms begin to slide over each other when a piece of wire is stretched. Up to the yield point the atoms are just displaced but will return to their original position when the force is removed.

Zwitterion Ions which can carry both positive or negative charge. e.g. amino acids.

Zygote What you get when an egg fuses with a sperm or a pollen grain nucleus fuses with an ovum. Zygotes usually have their chromosomes in pairs i.e. they are diploid.

Zymase A mixture of enzymes found in yeast which are involved in fermentation. Zymase catalyses the conversion of sugar to alcohol with the production of CO_2.

Some rules for writing S I units
1. A full stop is not needed after a unit except at the end of a sentence.
2. There is no plural form of a unit; e.g. 40 N, 70 kg.
3. Only the units named after famous scientists have capital initial letters; e.g. watts (W), newtons (N).

Physical quantity	Name of the S I unit		Given as S I units	Useful equations
length	metre	m		
Mass	kilogram	kg		
time	second	s		
electric current	ampere	A		$I = \dfrac{Q}{t}$
temperature	kelvin	K		
amount of substance	mole	mol		
work, (energy transfer)	joule	J	$kg\ m^2s^{-2}$	work = force x distance
force	newton	N	$kg\ m\ s^{-2}$	force = mass x acceleration
power	watt	W	$J\ s^{-1}$	$P = \dfrac{\text{Work done}}{\text{time}}$
speed		v	$m\ s^{-1}$	$speed = \dfrac{distance}{time}$
acceleration		a	$m\ s^{-2}$	$a = \dfrac{v-u}{t}$
quantity of electricity	coulomb	C or Q	A s	$Q = It$
potential difference	volt	V	joules per coulomb	$V = I R$
current	ampere	A	$C\ s^{-1}$	$I = \dfrac{Q}{t}$
resistance	ohm	R (Ω)		$R = \dfrac{V}{I}$
electrical power	watt	W		$P = I V$
sound		dB		
efficiency			(%)	$\dfrac{\text{work out x 100}}{\text{work in}}$
specific heat capacity			$J\ kg^{-1}\ K^{-1}$	$S.H.C. = \dfrac{energy}{mass \times \triangle T}$

Physical quantity	Name of the S I unit			Useful equations
pressure	pascal	Pa	$N\,m^{-2}$	$P = \dfrac{force}{area}$
density			$gram\ cm^{-3}$	$density = \dfrac{mass}{volume}$
momentum			$kg\,m\,s^{-1}$	
kinetic energy	joules	J	$kg\,m^2 s^{-2}$	$K.E. = \tfrac{1}{2}mv^2$
potential energy	joules	J	$kg\,m^2 s^{-2}$	$P.E. = m \times g \times height$
wavelength		(λ)	m	$\lambda = \dfrac{v}{n}$
frequency	hertz	Hz	(cycle per sec.)	

Some commonly-used letters from the Greek alphabet (with examples of their use)

A	$\propto$	alpha	as in alpha particle
B	β	beta	as in beta particle
Γ	γ	gamma	as in gamma rays
Δ	δ	delta	as in delta T (change in temperature)
Λ	λ	lambda	(used as the symbol for wavelength)
M	μ	mu	(used to stand for one millionth eg μ m.)
P	ρ	rho	(is used for density)
Σ	σ	sigma	(is used for 'the sum of' e.g. Σ v: the sum of all the velocities)